Newnes
Microprocessor Pocket Book

Newnes Microprocessor Pocket Book

Steve Money

Heinemann Newnes

Heinemann Newnes
An imprint of Heinemann Professional Publishing Ltd
Halley Court, Jordan Hill, Oxford OX2 8EJ

OXFORD LONDON MELBOURNE AUCKLAND SINGAPORE
IBADAN NAIROBI GABORONE KINGSTON

First published 1989

British Library Cataloguing in Publication Data
Money, Steve A.
  Newnes microprocessor pocket book.
  1. Microprocessor system
  I. Title
  004.16

ISBN 0 434 91290 5

Typeset by Electronic Village Ltd, Richmond, Surrey
Printed and bound in Great Britain by Courier International,
Tiptree, Essex

Contents

Preface

During the past ten years the microprocessor has become an integral part of many pieces of electronic equipment ranging from domestic appliances to industrial control systems. Compared with more conventional electronic systems using discrete components or integrated logic circuits the microprocessor has the advantage that it is versatile and can readily be adapted to perform a number of different functions merely by altering its programming. Another major advantage is that a microprocessor-based system often requires fewer components than the equivalent system based on more conventional electronic circuits.

The engineer involved in developing a system based around the use of a microprocessor needs to have some knowledge of programming as well as the usual knowledge of electronics circuit design. In a microprocessor system most of the functions that would normally be performed by logic circuits can be implemented by suitable instructions in the computer program or software. The result is that most of the hardware design is concerned with interfacing between the microprocessor and the outside world whilst the overall operation of the equipment is largely controlled by the software.

In this book the basic hardware operation of a microprocessor is explained and the actions of the various types of instruction that can be executed are described. In practice the instruction sets for the various types of microprocessor follow much the same pattern although the data sheet for the processor being used will generally need to be consulted to see exactly how the instruction is executed and which address modes are available.

A section of the book is devoted to a summary of the characteristics of many of the popular microprocessors in current use. There are in fact hundreds of types of microprocessor available and there are many variants of the ones described. In many cases the difference between types is in the speed of operation. Sometimes the alternative types may use a different fabrication technology or provide a few additional instructions or extra hardware features. To give details of every processor type would require a much larger book than this so coverage has been restricted to the basic processors of the more popular ranges. Details given include pin connections, signal functions, instruction set summary and details of timing and interrupt operation.

Apart from the popular 8- and 16-bit microprocessors some details are also given of the popular single chip microcomputers and of the more recently developed reduced instruction set computer (RISC) type processors such as the Transputer, Novix FORTH processor and Acorn ARM processor.

For most practical applications the microprocessor acts as a controller for the rest of the equipment but it could also be used for taking measurements in an instrumentation system. Usually a combination of these two basic functions is performed. In either case the connection or interface between the processor and the rest of the electronics is important. In this book the principles involved in both parallel and serial input-output interfaces are discussed. Details are given of the common standards used for parallel and serial input-output systems.

Although discrete logic can be used for input-output interfaces, most microprocessor-based systems use specially developed integrated circuits for this purpose. Examples of these special interface chips are described with details of their internal arrangement and the basic techniques for programming their modes of operation. This covers parallel and serial input-output chips, counters and timers as well as one or two of the multifunction peripheral chips that are available.

The development of a microprocessor-based system can be made easier by the use of a good microprocessor development system (MDS) which provides facilities for writing and testing the software. Most development systems also provide diagnostic tools, such as In Circuit Emulation, for testing the hardware design. The principles of development systems are described in this book. Although most systems use mnemonic assembly language for programming other higher level languages such as BASIC, FORTH and C are also used. The principles of these assembler, interpreter and compiler type languages are discussed together with the use of diagnostic routines such as debuggers.

Many microprocessor-based systems are designed

around the use of popular personal computers such as the IBM PC so the arrangement of the expansion bus for this machine is given. For industrial applications a system using standard cards plugged into a backframe bus system is often used. Typical buses are the STD, STE and Intel Multibus and details of these buses are given.

In this book I have tried to present a wide selection of information likely to be of general use to the engineer involved in developing a microprocessor-based system. It will also be of interest to anyone involved in designing, servicing or just wishing to learn more about microprocessor-based systems.

Steve Money

1 Integrated circuits

Integrated circuits are circuits composed of transistors, diodes, resistors and capacitors fabricated on a single chip of semiconductor material which is typically silicon. The circuits may be analogue types, such as amplifiers, or digital types such as logic gates, switches and memory devices. Integrated circuits can be broadly classified into a series of scales of integration according to their complexity.

Scales of integration

Early designs for digital integrated circuits contain the equivalent of up to about ten simple logic gates and are generally referred to as small scale integration (SSI) circuits. Examples of SSI chips are the basic transistor transistor logic (TTL) gates such as the 7400, 7410 and 7420.

As techniques improved larger devices with some 10 to 100 gates were produced. These are called medium scale integration (MSI) circuits. Examples of MSI circuits are the 4-bit binary counter devices such as the 74190, 74194 and 74196.

Further development of fabrication techniques allowed the production of large scale integration (LSI) circuits containing up to 1000 gates. Examples of LSI devices include the 8-bit microprocessors such as the Motorola 6800 and Zilog Z80. This level of integration also covers most of the microprocessor support chips and the smaller capacity memory devices.

More recently even larger circuits with more than 1000 gates have been produced. These are referred to as very large scale integration (VLSI) circuits and include the modern 16- and 32-bit microprocessors such as the Intel 8086 and Motorola 68000. Also included in this category are many of the large memory chips and some logic array chips which are used for custom designed digital circuits.

Normally a large array of separate integrated circuit chips is produced on a silicon wafer of perhaps 7.5 to 10 cm in diameter. The wafer is then cut up to produce separate chips which are packaged as individual integrated circuits. The latest development is wafer scale integration in which the array of chips on the wafer is left intact. Individual chips on the wafer are tested and those which work properly are wired together to form a complete system. This scheme allows the production of a memory array with enormous capacity in a single package. Alternatively a large array of interconnected microprocessors could be produced as a single integrated circuit.

Fabrication technologies

A variety of different fabrication technologies has been employed for making digital integrated circuits. These fall into two major groups: bipolars and metal oxide semiconductors (MOS).

Bipolar logic devices

This type of device uses conventional npn or pnp type junction transistors fabricated on a silicon wafer. They have the advantage of high switching speed but tend to require quite large levels of supply current and are not very tolerant of variations in the power supply voltage.

Diode transistor logic (DTL)

The gate structure for DTL uses diodes for the actual logic function with a transistor buffer amplifier to drive the output, as shown in Figure 1.

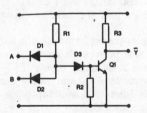

Figure 1 Circuit of a DTL-type AND gate

Typical of these devices were those in the 930 series which was produced by a number of different manufacturers. DTL is now obsolete although 930 series chips may be found in some older computer and industrial control equipment.

Supply voltage 4.5−5.5 V
Supply current (per gate) typical 4 mA
Gate delay time 30 nS max.
Input
   low +1.1 V max. −1.4 mA
   high +2.0 V min. 5 μA
Output
   low +0.45 V max. 12 mA
   high +2.6 V min. −120 μA

Transistor transistor logic (TTL)

The gate structure of TTL devices typically uses multi-emitter transistors for the gate action followed by a transistor amplifier to drive the output, as shown in Figure 2. This widely used logic family has device type numbers which start with the code 74. Most of the simpler circuits in the series, such as gates and flip-flops, have numbers in the series 7400 to 7499. Many more complex devices have numbers ranging from 74100 up to numbers in the region of 74900. Originally introduced by Texas Instruments, the TTL 74 series is now available from a large number of different manufacturers.

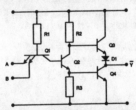

Figure 2 Circuit of a TTL-type AND gate

TTL devices have the advantage of quite high speed with typical gate delay times of the order 15 ns. When an input is held in its low or '0' state the circuit driving the input must be able to sink about 1.6 mA of current flowing from the gate input circuit. The output of a typical TTL device can sink a current of about 16 mA and will drive the inputs of up to ten other TTL gates.

The main disadvantage of standard TTL is that it requires a stable power supply, within 5% of the nominal +5 V which even for a relatively small system may have to supply currents in the order of amperes. Decoupling of the supply is also important and a 0.1 μF decoupling capacitor should be included across the supply lines close to every group of four to five TTL chips.

Supply voltage   +4.75 V−+5.25 V
Supply current (per gate) typical   4 mA
Gate delay time   15 ns
Input
  low   +0.8 V max. −1.6 mA
  high   +2.0 V min. 10 μA
Output
  low   +0.4 V max. 16 mA
  high   +2.4 V min. −400 μA

Low power TTL (LPTTL)

To overcome the power demands of standard TTL a modified version known as low power TTL was developed. These circuits offer a supply current demand much lower than that of standard TTL devices but this results in a lower switching speed. Gate delay for a typical 74L series gate is around 90 ns. Logic signal levels for LPTTL are the same as for TTL but input and output current levels are much lower. This range of circuits has type numbers prefixed with the code 74L and have equivalent functions to the corresponding 74 series device. Thus a 74L00 is the low power equivalent of the 7400.

Supply voltage   +4.75 V−+5.25 V
Supply current (per gate) typical   0.5 mA
Gate delay time   .90 ns
Input
  low   +0.7 V max. −0.18 mA
  high   +2.0 V min. 10 μA
Output
  low   +0.3 V max. 2 mA
  high   +2.4 V min. −100 μA

Schottky TTL (STTL)

By incorporating Schottky diodes into the input circuits of a TTL device it was found that the switching speed could be increased to give a typical gate delay of around 7 ns and flip-flop switching speeds up to 125 MHz. This type of logic provides equivalent devices to those in the standard TTL range but the type numbers are prefixed by the code 74S. The Schottky equivalent of a 7400 quad NAND gate is the 74S00.

Supply voltage + 4.75 V – + 5.25 V
Supply current (per gate) typical 6 mA
Gate delay time 7 ns typical
Input
  low +0.8 V max. −2 mA
  high +2.0 V min. 50 μA
Output
  low +0.5 V max. 20 mA
  high +3.4 V min. −1 mA

Low power Schottky TTL (LPSTTL)

The Schottky diode modification has also been
applied to low powered versions of TTL to produce
a range of devices with type numbers prefixed by
74LS. These have the advantage of similar speed to
the standard 74 series TTL types with about one-fifth
of the power consumption. Logic signal levels are the
same as for standard TTL. Most modern logic
systems tend to use the 74LS series devices in
preference to standard 74 series TTL.

Supply voltage +4.75 V – +5.25 V
Supply current (per gate) typical 0.4 mA
Gate delay time 15 ns typical
Input
  low +0.8 V max. −0.4 mA
  high +2.0 V min. 40 μA
Output
  low +0.5 V max. 8 mA
  high +2.4 V min. −400 μA

A new development of Schottky devices is the
advanced low power Schottky range with 74ALS type
numbers. These have the advantage of being roughly
twice as fast in operation as the normal 74LS types
and have about half the supply current requirements.

High speed TTL (HTTL)

This range of devices with 74H type numbers is
designed for high-speed switching with typical speeds
of 6 ns for a gate. The range of functions available
includes most of the more popular circuits of the
standard TTL range. A disadvantage is that power
requirements for the 74H series are higher than for
standard 74 type TTL.

Supply voltage   +4.75–+5.25 V
Supply current (per gate) typical   5 mA
Gate delay time   6 ns
Input
  low   +0.8 V max. −2 mA
  high   +2.0 V min. 50 µA
Output
  low   +0.4 V max. 20 mA
  high   +2.4 V min. −500 µA

Fairchild advanced Schottky TTL (FTTL)

Like HTTL these devices are designed for high speed
but have the advantage of low power consumption.
Most of the standard circuits are available with type
numbers in the 74F series. Speed is similar to that of
the 74S series but with power consumption only
about twice that of the 74LS series.

Supply voltage   +4.75 V–+5.25 V
Supply current (per gate) typical   0.9 mA
Gate delay time   7.5 ns
Input
  low   +0.8 V max. −0.6 mA
  high   +2.0 V min. 20 µA
Output
  low   +0.4 V max. 24 mA
  high   +2.4 V min. 200 µA

Other bipolar types

Two other types of bipolar circuits which have
been used for logic devices are emitter coupled
logic (ECL) and integrated injection logic (IIL or
I^2L). The main advantage of ECL is its very high
switching speed with typical gate delays of the
order 3 ns. A typical range of ECL devices is the
Motorola MC10000 series which includes a bit
slice microprocessor. Unlike TTL these devices
operate with a −5.2 V supply. Interface circuits
are available which will convert the ECL logic
signals to normal TTL levels. This type of logic is
generally limited to use in very high speed applications such as counters and gates for use in
frequency synthesizers used in VHF or UHF radio
systems.
    The IIL type devices are often used in calculator
chips and have been used for some microprocessors

in the Texas 9900 series. These circuits provide speeds similar to those of TTL but with lower power consumption.

Metal oxide semiconductor devices

The alternative to the bipolar type circuit is one which uses insulated gate field effect transistors as the active elements. These are built up using metal oxide on semiconductor MOS fabrication techniques.

P-channel metal oxide semiconductor (PMOS)

This type of logic uses P-channel insulated gate field effect transistors to make up the gates and flip-flop circuits. Most modern PMOS circuits operate from a single -10 V power supply but some early types required a positive supply rail as well. This type of circuit is slow compared with a bipolar one such as TTL but requires relatively little supply current. The inputs have very high impedance and a major problem with early PMOS devices was their susceptibility to static electicity. Static charges can be produced when handling the chip and if discharged via an input to the chip could easily destroy a gate. Modern PMOS circuits include protection diodes but still need careful handling to avoid damage. PMOS devices are not generally used for discrete logic gates or flip-flops but are used for some 4-bit microcomputers. With a power supply of -10 V the logic voltage levels are negative and give a signal swing of perhaps 8–10 V. Logic level converters are needed to interface PMOS circuits to systems which use TTL signal levels.

N-channel metal oxide semiconductor (NMOS)

In this type of circuit N-channel field effect transistors are used to build the gate and flip-flop elements. The NMOS type circuit is faster in operation than an equivalent PMOS version but was initially more difficult to manufacture. Some early devices required both positive and negative power supplies but modern NMOS devices are designed to operate from a single $+5$ V supply and the biassing arrangements are dealt with inside the chip.

Although a few small scale circuits were produced the NMOS type of logic circuit is generally used in

LSI and VLSI devices such as microprocessors, complex support chips and memories. Most of the common 8-bit microprocessors such as the Z80, 6809, 6502 and 8085 use NMOS technology. The 16-bit types use modified forms of NMOS to give faster operation and more complex circuitry on the chip.

The switching speed depends upon the geometry of the circuits on the chip but is generally slower than for bipolar type circuits. Current requirements are relatively low and power supply tolerance tends to be similar to that for TTL devices. The inputs have very high impedance and need protection from damage by static electric charges. All modern NMOS chips include static protection diodes on their input lines. Most types operate from a +5 V power supply and logic levels are generally compatible with TTL type devices.

Complementary metal oxide semiconductor (CMOS)

This logic technology uses a combination of N-channel and P-channel field effect transistors to produce its gates and the typical CMOS gate structure is as shown in Figure 3. A standard range of CMOS logic devices was originally introduced by RCA with type numbers in the 4000 series. CMOS logic is now produced by several manufacturers who use different prefix letters in front of the 4000 series code. A further series of CMOS devices with numbers in the 4500 series is also widely used.

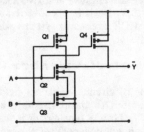

Figure 3 Circuit of a CMOS-type AND gate

Supply voltage +3 V–+15 V
Gate delay time 90 ns typical
Input
  low   +1.5 V max. 10 pA
  high   +3.5 V min. 10 pA

Output

    low   +0.05 V max. 1 mA
    high   +4.95 V min. −1 mA

These figures are based on a supply voltage of +5 V. With a supply voltage of 10–15 V, the speed and output current are roughly double those for a 5 V supply. When circuits are in a static state the supply current is extremely small. When circuits are being switched the supply current rises as the switching rate increases.

An alternative series of CMOS logic devices was introduced by some manufacturers to give pin and function compatibility with the 74 series TTL devices. These circuits were given type numbers starting with 74C so that a 74C00 would be the CMOS equivalent of a 7400 in TTL.

New high speed versions are available in the 74HC series which has CMOS compatible inputs and the 74HCT series which has TTL compatible inputs. For these types the output current capability is increased to 4 mA and gate delay times are typically 10 nS. The latest series of CMOS devices is the 74AC series. These provide typical propagation delays per gate of 5 nS and can provide output current drives of 24 mA.

CMOS has the advantage that it draws virtually no supply current when the circuit is not switching and hence the power supply current requirements can be very small. CMOS devices also have the advantage that the power supply voltage is not critical as it is for TTL so that a typical CMOS device will work on a supply voltage which may vary from perhaps 4 V to 8 V. These two factors make CMOS logic highly suited for portable battery operated equipment.

Input impedance is extremely high, in the order of tens of megohms, and static protection diodes are normally included on all input lines. A CMOS output can typically drive a large number of CMOS device input lines. When used on a +5 V supply the low state is typically 0 V and the high state +5 V unless the device is heavily loaded. An input treats any signal below about +2.5 V as low and signals above that level as high. Typical gate delay times for standard 4000 series CMOS devices are around 30 ns giving a speed comparable with the old DTL devices.

Variants of the basic CMOS technique are used by a number of manufacturers to produce high density LSI and VLSI circuits for microprocessors, memories and other support chips.

Handling precautions for MOS devices

All of the logic devices based on MOS technology
have extremely high impedance input circuits and are
susceptible to damage from static electric charges.
These circuits should be stored with their pins effectively shorted together by inserting the pins into a pad
of conductive plastic or a sheet of metal foil. Before
handling such devices the user should first discharge
any static charges on their body or the tools being
used by grounding them. Most chips now include
protection diodes across their inputs to reduce the
possibility of damage by static charges but it is wise
to take precautions to avoid static charge build up
even with these protected types.

Circuit boards containing MOS devices should be
handled in a similar fashion to avoid damage to the
integrated circuits on the board. On circuit boards
using MOS devices it is useful to include resistors of
perhaps 100k to ground from each input line to
prevent static build up.

Logic functions

In digital circuits each signal may take up one of two
logic states. The low voltage state is generally referred
to as the '0' or 'low' level and the high voltage state
is known as the '1' or 'high' level. These logic signals
may be combined together and operated upon by
electronic circuits called logic gates. Typically a gate
will have two or more inputs and a single output.

There are three basic logic functions known as
AND, OR and EXCLUSIVE OR. A fourth type of
circuit that is available is the buffer whose output is
the same as its input. Figure 4 shows the symbols
normally used to represent these basic gate devices.

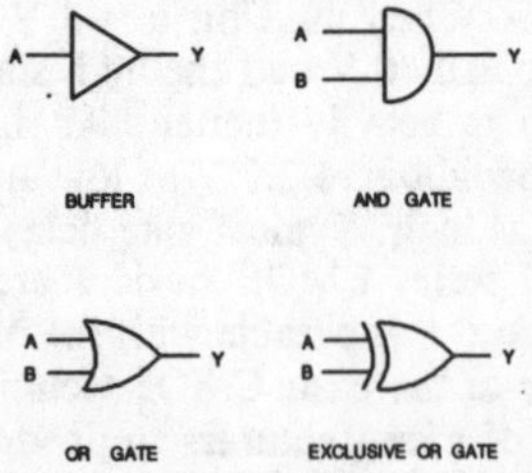

BUFFER   AND GATE

OR GATE   EXCLUSIVE OR GATE

Figure 4 Symbols for AND, OR and XOR gates

In the AND gate the output goes to 1 only when all of the inputs are at 1. Thus for a gate with two inputs A and B the output is 1 only when A AND B are both at 1. The truth table giving the four possible states of a two input AND gate is shown in Figure 5.

INPUT A	INPUT B	OUTPUT
0	0	0
0	1	0
1	0	0
1	1	1

Figure 5   Truth table for a 2 input AND gate

The second simple type of gate is the OR in which the output goes to 1 when any input is at 1. A point to note here is that the output is only at 0 when both inputs are at 0. The truth table for the four possible states of a two input OR gate is shown in Figure 6.

INPUT A	INPUT B	OUTPUT
0	0	0
0	1	1
1	0	1
1	1	1

Figure 6   Truth table for a 2 input OR gate

The EXCLUSIVE OR gate unlike the simple OR type gives an output of 1 when only one of the inputs is at 1. This type of gate is often referred to as an XOR gate. The truth table for the four possible states of a two input EXCLUSIVE OR gate is shown in Figure 7.

INPUT A	INPUT B	OUTPUT
0	0	0
0	1	1
1	0	1
1	1	0

Figure 7   Truth table for a 2 input exclusive OR gate

When the two inputs of the EXCLUSIVE OR gate have the same state the output of the gate goes to 0. This makes this type of gate useful for detecting matches between bits on pairs of input signals.

The fourth simple logic function is a buffer whose output has the same logic state as its input. Buffers generally have the capability of driving more gate inputs than a standard logic gate. Some buffers are designed to change the logic voltage levels to match a different family of logic devices or to drive lamps or relays.

An alternative type of logic circuit is one where the output stage inverts the logic state. In the case of a buffer the circuit becomes an inverter or NOT gate where a 1 at the input produces a 0 at the output. To indicate the inversion the NOT gate has a small circle drawn at its output point. The AND, OR and XOR type gates can also be produced with inverted outputs to become NAND, NOR and XNOR gates respectively. The logic symbols for these inverted output gates are shown in Figure 8.

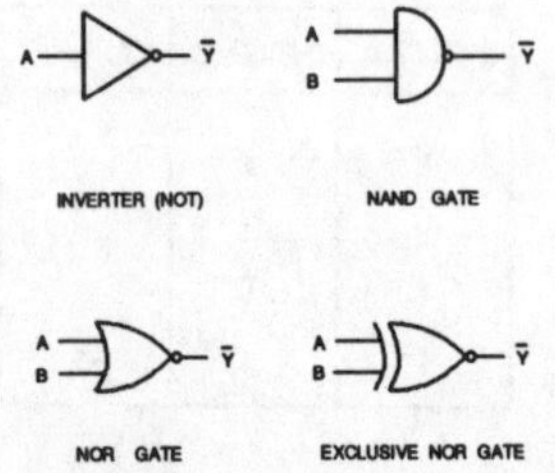

INVERTER (NOT)   NAND GATE

NOR GATE   EXCLUSIVE NOR GATE

Figure 8 Symbols for gates with inverted outputs

Figure 9 shows the truth table for a two input NOT AND or NAND gate. Here the output is normally at 1 and goes to 0 only when both inputs are at 1. In the truth table for the NOR gate the output goes to 0 when either of the two inputs is at 1, as shown in Figure 10. When the output of an EXCLUSIVE OR gate is inverted it becomes an EXCLUSIVE NOR or XNOR gate and has the truth table shown in Figure 11.

Flip-flop circuits

Apart from gates the other widely used logic circuit is the flip-flop. In its simplest form this circuit consists of two transistors cross connected as shown

INPUT A	INPUT B	OUTPUT
0	0	1
0	1	1
1	0	1
1	1	0

Figure 9 Truth table for a 2 input NAND gate

INPUT A	INPUT B	OUTPUT
0	0	1
0	1	0
1	0	0
1	1	0

Figure 10 Truth table for a 2 input NOR gate

INPUT A	INPUT B	OUTPUT
0	0	1
0	1	0
1	0	0
1	1	1

Figure 11 Truth table for a 2 input exclusive NOR gate

in Figure 12. The circuit has two stable states in which one transistor is on and the other is off. By applying a pulse to the SET or RESET input the circuit can be switched to either state as desired. This simple flip-flop circuit is referred to as a set–reset (S–R) flip-flop.

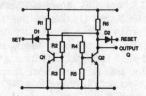

Figure 12 Flip-flop circuit using transistors

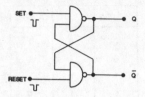

Figure 13 Flip-flop using NAND gates

In integrated circuits the flip-flop action is generally produced by cross connecting gates and several types of flip-flop circuit may be produced. The logic symbols for some of these circuits are shown in Figure 14.

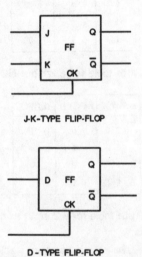

J-K-TYPE FLIP-FLOP

D-TYPE FLIP-FLOP

Figure 14 Symbols used for J–K and D-type flip-flops

For a J–K flip-flop the action of the output line Q when a clock pulse is applied depends upon the states of the J and K inputs as shown in Figure 15. In the D flip-flop the output Q takes up the same state as the D input when a clock pulse is applied.

A flip-flop can be arranged to change its state each time a clock pulse is applied and its output will be a square wave at half the input clock frequency. This divide by two action is achieved in a J–K flip-flop by setting both J and K at 1. In the case of a D-type flip-flop the same result is achieved by connecting the

J	K	OUTPUT Q
0	0	NO CHANGE
1	0	0
0	1	1
1	1	$\overline{Q}$

Figure 15 Truth table for a J–K flip-flop

inverted Q output to the D input. If several divide by
two stages are connected in cascade a counter can be
produced since each stage divides the input by two
and the states of the set of flip-flops will give a binary
count of the number of pulses applied at the initial
input. By using gates to provide feedback a four stage
counter chain can be arranged to act as a decade
counter which produces an output pulse for every ten
clock pulses at the input.

A variation on the flip-flop is the monostable
circuit where one of the feedback paths in the basic
flip-flip is replaced by a resistor–capacitor (RC)
circuit. Now the circuit has only one stable state.
When the circuit is triggered it still switches states in
much the same way as a flip-flop but after a period
of time the capacitor charges, or discharges, and
allows the circuit to flop back into its original stable
state. The monostable circuit therefore produces a
pulse at its output and the duration of the pulse is
governed by the values used in the RC network.

A simple monostable circuit will ignore any further
input trigger signals once it has been triggered and
will produce a fixed time delay before it resets to its
stable state. An alternative type is the retriggerable
monostable which restarts its timing cycle each time
a new input pulse is applied. Thus if a new trigger
input is applied whilst the monostable is in its set
state the timing restarts and the total delay time is
increased.

74 and 4000 series logic devices

Some of the wide range of logic types available in the
74 series TTL and 4000 series CMOS are are listed
below.

1 Gates and buffers

7400	Quad 2-input NAND
7401	Quad 2-input NOR (open collector output [o.c.])
7402	Quad 2-input NOR
7403	Quad 2-input NAND (o.c.)
7404	Hex inverter
7405	Hex inverter (o.c.)
7406	Hex inverter (o.c.) high volt o/p
7407	Hex buffer (o.c.) high volt o/p
7408	Quad 2-input AND
7409	Quad 2-input AND (o.c.)
7410	Triple 3-input NAND
7411	Triple 3-input AND
7412	Triple 3-input NAND (o.c.)
7414	Hex Schmitt inverter
7415	Triple 3-input AND (o.c.)
7416	Hex inverter (o.c.)
7417	Hex buffer (o.c.)
7420	Dual 4-input NAND
7421	Dual 4-input AND
7422	Dual 4-input NAND (o.c.)
7426	Quad 2-input NAND (o.c.)
7427	Triple 3-input NOR
7428	Quad 2-input NOR buffer
7430	8 input NAND
7432	Quad 2-input OR
7433	Quad 2-input NOR buffer (o.c.)
7440	Dual 4-input NAND buffer
7450	Dual AND-OR-NOT
7460	Dual 4-input expander
7486	Quad 2-input XOR
74125	Quad buffer (tristate)
74126	Quad buffer (tristate)
74133	13-input NAND
74134	12-input NAND (tristate)
74136	Quad 2-input XOR

2 Bus Transceivers

74226	4-bit latched
74242	4-bit inverting (tristate)
74243	4-bit non-inverting (tristate)
74245	8-bit non-inverting (tristate)

3 Flip-flops and latches

7470	J–K flip-flop
7472	J–K flip-flop
7473	Dual J–K flip-flop
7474	Dual D-type flip-flop
7475	Quad latch
7476	Dual J–K flip-flop
7477	Quad D latch
74107	Dual J–K flip-flop
74109	Dual J–K flip-flop
74112	Dual J–K flip-flop
74118	Hex S–R latch
74173	Quad D latch (tristate)
74174	Hex D flip-flop
74175	Quad D flip-flop
74273	Octal D flip-flop
74279	Quad S–R latch
74373	Octal D latch
74374	Octal D flip-flop
74377	Octal D flip-flop
4013	Dual D flip-flop
4027	Dual J–K flip-flop
4042	Quad D latch
4043	Quad S–R latch (tristate)
4044	Quad S–R latch (tristate)
4508	Quad D latch (tristate)

4 Counters

7490	Decade counter
7492	Divide by twelve
7493	4-bit binary
74160	Decade with preset
74161	4-bit up/down with preset
74163	4-bit up/down with preset
74169	4-bit up/down with preset
74190	Decade up/down with preset
74191	4-bit up/down with preset
74192	Decade up/down with preset
74193	4-bit up/down with preset
74197	4-bit with preset
74390	Dual decade counter
74393	Dual 4-bit counter
74490	Dual decade counter
4017	Decimal with decoded outputs
4020	14-bit binary counter
4024	7-bit binary counter

4022	Octal with decoded outputs
4029	4-bit or decade counter
4040	12-bit binary counter
4060	14-bit binary counter
40103	8-bit binary counter
4510	Decade up/down with preset

5 Decoders/demultiplexers

7442	4 to 10 line
74137	3 to 8 line
74138	3 to 8 line
74139	Dual 2 to 4 line
74141	4 to 10 line
74145	4 to 10 line
74154	4 to 16 line
74155	Dual 2 to 4 line
74237	3 to 8 line
74238	3 to 8 line
4028	4 to 10 line
4514	4 to 16 line
4555	Dual 2 to 4 line

6 Multiplexers

74150	16-input
74151	8-input
74153	Dual 4-input
74157	Quad 2-input
74158	Quad 2-input
74251	8-input
74257	Quad 2-input
74352	Dual 4-input
74354	8-input
74356	8-input
4512	8-input

7 Monostable circuits

74121	Single monostable
74122	Single retriggerable monostable
74123	Dual retriggerable monostable
74221	Dual monostable
4047	Single retriggerable monostable
4098	Dual retriggerable monostable
4528	Dual resetable monostable

2 Data formats

In an electronic logic system the signals have two switched states which are usually represented by a high or low voltage. These are referred to as 0 or low for the low voltage state and 1 or high for the high voltage level. In some cases the 0 state may be called false and the 1 state true.

A single logic signal can be used to represent the numbers 0 and 1. To deal with larger numbers several logic signals are taken in combination to represent the desired number. In this case each signal is referred to as a binary digit or 'bit'. The combination of a set of bits to represent a number is referred to as a 'word'. A data word composed of a set of 8 bits is normally called a 'byte' whilst the name 'nybble' is often used to describe a 4-bit word.

If we consider a word of 4 bits there are a total of sixteen different combinations of 0 and 1 states for the set of 4-bits, as shown in Figure 16, and the 4-bit word could be used to represent the numbers from 0 to 15. If an 8-bit word is used the number range 0 to 255 could be represented. When 16-bits are used the number of combinations rises to 65,536 whilst a 32-bit word can produce over 16 million possible combinations. Microprocessors generally use 8-, 16- or 32-bit words to represent numbers or other data.

BINARY BITS B3 B2 B1 B0	NUMBER UNSIGNED	NUMBER SIGNED
0 0 0 0	0	0
0 0 0 1	1	1
0 0 1 0	2	2
0 0 1 1	3	3
0 1 0 0	4	4
0 1 0 1	5	5
0 1 1 0	6	6
0 1 1 1	7	7
1 0 0 0	8	-8
1 0 0 1	9	-7
1 0 1 0	10	-6
1 0 1 1	11	-5
1 1 0 0	12	-4
1 1 0 1	13	-3
1 1 1 0	14	-2
1 1 1 1	15	-1

Figure 16 Representation of numbers using 4-data bits

Decimal numbers

The number system which we are all familiar with in everyday life is the decimal system in which each digit can have one of ten possible values from 0 to 9. Each digit in a number also represents a power of ten so that working from right to left the digits represent units (10^0), tens (10^1), hundreds (10^2), thousands (10^3) and so on.

Binary numbers

In a computer system the data word is generally used to represent a number in pure binary form. In this system each bit is given a weight corresponding to a power of two. Working from right to left the individual bits represent units (2^0), twos (2^1), fours (2^2), eights (2^3) and so on as shown in Figure 17. To evaluate a binary word the weighted values of all the bits that are in the 1 state are added together. Bits at the 0 state have the value 0. Thus the binary number 1010 is $1 \times 8 + 1 \times 2$ giving the decimal value 10.

Figure 17 Weighting of the bits in an 8-bit binary word

When written down a binary number consists of a string of 0 or 1 digits so that the number 70 in decimal would be written as %1000110 in the binary format. In program listings for assembler and some high-level languages it is usual to write a % in front of a binary number to differentiate it from a normal decimal number.

The bit at the right-hand end of the binary word is referred to as the least significant bit (LSB) and that at the left hand end is called the most significant bit (MSB).

Octal numbers

For large numbers the pure binary notation is not very convenient and results in long strings of digits.

Most users are used to decimal numbers and are unlikely to appreciate the values of large numbers written in binary form. An alternative way of writing down large binary numbers is to express them in octal form.

In octal form the number is represented to the base eight (octal) and each digit of the number may range from 0 to 7. To convert from binary to octal take the binary bits in groups of three starting from the right-hand end and write down the equivalent octal value of the three binary bits in each group. Thus for the decimal number 70 we have the binary pattern 1 000 110 which is split into groups of three bits to give 1 000 110 and this is written in octal form as /106. Octal numbers are generally indicated by prefixing them with a / symbol.

Hexadecimal numbers

Although octal is a convenient way of writing down large binary numbers a more popular scheme is to write the numbers in hexadecimal form where numbers are represented to a base of sixteen.

To convert from binary to hexadecimal the binary bits are divided into groups of 4 bits for each hexadecimal digit. Thus for the decimal number 70 the binary pattern is split into two groups 100 0110 and the hexadecimal value becomes $46.

Each hexadecimal digit can have a value from 0 to 15 in decimal. For the values from 0 to 9 the normal figure symbols 0 to 9 are used whilst the values from 10 to 15 are represented by the letters A to F respectively.

To differentiate hexadecimal numbers from the normal decimal format they are usually written with a $ sign in front. Thus the number 31 in decimal would be written as $1F in hexadecimal. An alternative method of denoting a hexadecimal number is to write an H after it so that $1F becomes 1FH.

Binary coded decimal

Although binary, octal and hexadecimal are convenient ways of representing the binary data held in the computer memory the number system which we use in everyday life is decimal and it is convenient to input and output numbers in the decimal format. Conversions from decimal to binary and vice versa are relatively complex and a more convenient method of representing decimal numbers in the computer is to use the binary coded decimal (BCD) scheme.

In the BCD format each decimal digit of the number is represented as a group of 4-bit binary bits. Thus if we have the decimal number 234 it would be stored as 0010 0011 0100. Conversion between BCD and decimal for input and output of data is now relatively simple since each set of 4-bits representing a BCD digit can be translated directly into its decimal equivalent.

Signed binary numbers

In a computer the binary number held in a computer word can simply be considered as a positive number from 0 to 255 for an 8-bit word or from 0 to 65535 for a 16-bit word.

For practical applications there is a need to be able to represent negative values. The scheme generally used for signed numbers is complemented binary in which the most significant digit of the number indicates the sign of the number.

In an 8-bit system if 1 is added to the highest number (255) the result is that all the bits change to 0 and a carry bit is produced which represents a ninth binary bit. On this basis if 1 is subtracted from 0 to give the value −1 the result in an 8-bit system would be 255 or all bits set at 1. In this number the most significant bit is 1 and this can be treated as a sign indicator. Thus numbers from 0 to 127 which have the MSB at 0 would represent the positive values 0 to 127. Numbers in the range 128 to 255 where the MSB is 1 would represent the negative values from −1 (255) to −128 (128). This is demonstrated as follows:

Binary	Decimal
0111111	+127
0111110	+126
0000100	+4
0000011	+3
0000010	+2
0000001	+1
0000000	0
1111111	−1
1111110	−2
1111101	−3

1111100	−4
1000010	−126
1000001	−127
1000000	−128

When numbers in this format are added or subtracted the correct signed result is produced and this is the form of binary arithmetic commonly used in microprocessor systems.

Floating point numbers

Normally the number represented by a computer data word is an integer value and its maximum value is limited by the number of bits in the word. For calculations in the real world a much larger range of values including fractional values is generally required. Remember that an 8-bit word has a maximum value of only 255.

The solution to this problem is to use floating point arithmetic. In this scheme the number is represented by perhaps two or three data words. One part is the mantissa which represents a fractional value between 0 and 1.0. The other part of the data is the exponent which acts as a scaling multiplier. This is the power of ten by which the mantissa must be multiplied to give the correct numerical value for the data.

Suppose we wish to represent the number 2000. This can be written as 0.2×10^4. Here the exponent would have the value 4 and the mantissa would be 0.2. For a fractional value the exponent becomes negative so with a mantissa of 0.2 and an exponent of -2 the value becomes 0.2×10^{-2} which is 0.2×0.01 giving a value of 0.002. For negative numbers the mantissa value is made negative using the normal signed binary format.

Incrementing the exponent is equivalent to multiplying the number by ten and decrementing the exponent produces a division by ten. With an 8-bit exponent numbers from 10^{-128} up to 10^{127} can be handled. The precision of the numbers is determined by the size of the mantissa word and for a 16-bit mantissa results would be represented to four significant digits in decimal form.

With floating point numbers where the exponent is based on ten it is often convenient to handle both the mantissa and the exponent as BCD numbers in the computer since this makes the arithmetic operations more straighforward. This form of floating point system is convenient where input and output data is normally in decimal format.

An alternative scheme is to have the exponent based on two rather than ten. This makes binary arithmetic on the exponent and mantissa more straightforward and is convenient in control systems where both input and output numbers can be in binary format.

Text data

A computer system is often required to be able to handle text data as, for instance, in a word processing program. A data word can readily be used to represent text symbols rather than numbers by allocating a different bit pattern to each text symbol. Thus twenty-five patterns would be needed to represent the letters A to Z with a further twenty-five for the lower case letters and ten more for the numeric symbols 0 to 9. When a selection of punctuation symbols and some control codes are added a typical symbol set would have perhaps 128 different symbol codes.

Generally, text symbols are held in the computer as 8-bit data words. Using 8-bits, a total of 256 different symbols can be represented although in practice most systems use only 7 of the 8-bits to give a standard 128 symbol set. Some computers use the most significant (eighth) bit to select an extended character set which might include Greek or mathematical symbols.

The standard code used by all microcomputer systems is International Standards Organisation Code No 7 (ISO7) which is based on the American Standard Code for Information Interchange (ASCII). In the international version some codes are used to represent alternative symbols to suit national language requirements.

The code provides upper and lower case letters, figures and a selection of punctuation signs. The first thirty-two codes are used for control purposes and do not normally produce a character on the display screen or print out.

ASCII code table

Decimal	Symbol	Binary	Hex.	Octal
0	NUL	0000000	00	000
1	SOH	0000001	01	001
2	STX	0000010	02	002
3	ETX	0000011	03	003
4	EOT	0000100	04	004
5	ENQ	0000101	05	005
6	ACK	0000110	06	006
7	BEL	0000111	07	007
8	BS	0001000	08	010
9	HT	0001001	09	011
10	LF	0001010	0A	012
11	VT	0001011	0B	013
12	FF	0001100	0C	014
13	CR	0001101	0D	015
14	SO	0001110	0E	016
15	SI	0001111	0F	017
16	DLE	0010000	10	020
17	DC1	0010001	11	021
18	DC2	0010010	12	022
19	DC3	0010011	13	023
20	DC4	0010100	14	024
21	NAK	0010101	15	025
22	SYN	0010110	16	026
23	ETB	0010111	17	027
24	CAN	0011000	18	030
25	EM	0011001	19	031
26	SUB	0011010	1A	032
27	ESC	0011011	1B	033
28	FS	0011100	1C	034
29	GS	0011101	1D	035
30	RS	0011110	1E	036
31	US	0011111	1F	037
32	space	0100000	20	040
33	!	0100001	21	041
34	"	0100010	22	042
35	#	0100011	23	043
36	$	0100100	24	044
37	%	0100101	25	045
38	&	0100110	26	046
39	'	0100111	27	047
40	(	0101000	28	050
41	)	0101001	29	051
42	*	0101010	2A	052

43	+	0101011	2B	053
44	,	0101100	2C	054
45	-	0101101	2D	055
46	.	0101110	2E	056
47	/	0101111	2F	057
48	0	0110000	30	060
49	1	0110001	31	061
50	2	0110010	32	062
51	3	0110011	33	063
52	4	0110100	34	064
53	5	0110101	35	065
54	6	0110110	36	066
55	7	0110111	37	067
56	8	0111000	38	070
57	9	0111001	39	071
58	:	0111010	3A	072
59	;	0111011	3B	073
60	<	0111100	3C	074
61	=	0111101	3D	075
62	>	0111110	3E	076
63	?	0111111	3F	077
64	@	1000000	40	100
65	A	1000001	41	101
66	B	1000010	42	102
67	C	1000011	43	103
68	D	1000100	44	104
69	E	1000101	45	105
70	F	1000110	46	106
71	G	1000111	47	107
72	H	1001000	48	110
73	I	1001001	49	111
74	J	1001010	4A	112
75	K	1001011	4B	113
76	L	1001100	4C	114
77	M	1001101	4D	115
78	N	1001110	4E	116
79	O	1001111	4F	117
80	P	1010000	50	120
81	Q	1010001	51	121
82	R	1010010	52	122
83	S	1010011	53	123
84	T	1010100	54	124
85	U	1010101	55	125
86	V	1010110	56	126
87	W	1010111	57	127
88	X	1011000	58	130
89	Y	1011001	59	131
90	Z	1011010	5A	132

91	[	1011011	5B	133
92	\	1011100	5C	134
93	]	1011101	5D	135
94	^	1011110	5E	136
95	_	1011111	5F	137
96	`	1100000	60	140
97	a	1100001	61	141
98	b	1100010	62	142
99	c	1100011	63	143
100	d	1100100	64	144
101	e	1100101	65	145
102	f	1100110	66	146
103	g	1100111	67	147
104	h	1101000	68	150
105	i	1101001	69	151
106	j	1101010	6A	152
107	k	1101011	6B	153
108	l	1101100	6C	154
109	m	1101101	6D	155
110	n	1101110	6E	156
111	o	1101111	6F	157
112	p	1110000	70	160
113	q	1110001	71	161
114	r	1110010	72	162
115	s	1110011	73	163
116	t	1110100	74	164
117	u	1110101	75	165
118	v	1110110	76	166
119	w	1110111	77	167
120	x	1111000	78	170
121	y	1111001	79	171
122	z	1111010	7A	172
123	{	1111011	7B	173
124	|	1111100	7C	174
125	}	1111101	7D	175
126	~	1111110	7E	176
127	DEL	1111111	7F	177

In Britain the code $23 is generally used for the pound sign instead of the # which appears in the US version of the code. Versions for other European countries include various accent symbols used in their native language. Printers generally have alternative character sets which may be selected to cater for these differences.

ASCII control codes

Hex-code	Abbreviation	Function
00	NUL	Null
		Fill character which is not printed
01	SOH	Start of header
		Marks start of header in a frame
02	STX	Start of text
		Marks start of message part of frame
03	ETX	End of text
		Marks end of message part of frame
04	EOT	End of transmission
05	ENQ	Enquiry
		Requests response from remote station
06	ACK	Acknowledge
		Confirms frame received OK
07	BEL	Bell
		Sounds bell or buzzer
08	BS	Backspace
		Move back one character position
09	HT	Horizontab tab
		Move to next tab stop
0A	LF	Line feed
		Move down to next line
0B	VT	Vertical tab
		Move down to next tab line
0C	FF	Form feed
		Go to new page
0D	CR	Carriage return
		Return to start of line
0E	SO	Shift out
		Select alternative character set
8F	SI	Shift in
		Select normal character set
10	DLE	Data link escape
		Changes meaning of next symbol code
11	DC1	Device control 1
		Used to control remote unit
12	DC2	Device control 2
		Used to control remote unit
13	DC3	Device control 3

		Used to control remote unit
14	DC4	Device control 4
		Used to control remote unit
15	NAK	Negative acknowledge
		Used to indicate an error in reception
16	SYN	Synchronization code
		Idle pattern to maintain synchronization
17	ETB	End of transmission block
		Indicates end of a frame
18	CAN	Cancel
		Cancel line (all back to last CR)
19	EM	End of medium
		Signals end of paper or tape
1A	SUB	Substitute
		Replace previous character
1B	ESC	Escape
		Select different meaning for following codes
1C	FS	Field separator
1D	GS	Group separator
1E	RS	Record separator
1F	US	Unit separator
7F	DEL	Delete
		Erase the previous symbol

FS, GS, RS and US are used as markers to separate various sections of a text or data file.

DLE is used in a stream of binary code data words to indicate that the following word should be interpreted as a control code and not as data.

ESC may be used to select either a different character set or an alternative control function.

HT and VT are used to move to the next horizontal or vertical tab position for laying out tabular information on the printed or displayed page.

CR moves the cursor or print head to the start of the line whilst LF moves the cursor or printer down to the next line. Normally both CR and LF are sent at the end of a line. The system may be set up so that the printer or screen display automatically carries out the line feed action when a CR code is received in which case only the CR code would be sent.

3 Microcomputer hardware

A digital computer whether it be a microprocessor or a mainframe computer will generally consist of a central processing unit (CPU), some input and output channels and a memory unit which holds the program instructions and data. These are linked together by three bus systems, as shown in Figure 18.

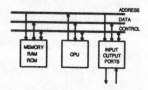

Figure 18 Block diagram of parts of a micro-computer

A microprocessor chip contains only the CPU section and by itself is of little use. To make a working microcomputer some memory and input–output channels need to be added to the basic microprocessor device. All of the widely used general purpose microprocessor chips such as the Z80, 6502, 6809 and 68000 fall into this category.

As an alternative to the simple microprocessor it is possible to build a chip which contains the CPU, some memory and one or more input–output channels. This type of chip is generally referred to as a single chip microcomputer. Normally microcomputer chips will contain some read-only memory (ROM) to hold the program instructions and a small random access read/write memory (RAM) to hold data and variable information. For mass production applications the ROM is usually mask programmed so that the computer program data is built permanently into the chip when it is manufactured. Some microcomputer chips are built with a ROM that is field programmable and the user then writes the required program data into the chip before installing it in a system. For development work and applications where only a small number of units are to be built an erasable ROM may be used in which the contents can be erased using ultraviolet light and then reprogrammed with new information. Single chip microcomputers are widely used in consumer equiment such as washing machines, microwave ovens, video recorders and even in toys. Another name sometimes used for this type of chip is microcontroller.

A variation of the general-purpose microprocessor is the digital signal processor (DSP) which is designed for high-speed signal processing applications such as digital filters, Fourier analysis, autocorrelation and digital image processing. Such computations require operations such as multiply and add applied to vast arrays of data and the DSP device is designed to perform such calculations at many times the speed of a general-purpose microprocessor.

Another variation on microprocessor construction is the bit slice processor in which the CPU section itself is divided up into separate chips. Here the registers and arithmetic circuits may be divided into 4-bit wide sections, each on a separate chip. These 4-bit wide slices of the CPU are assembled together to provide the desired word length. An example of this type of processor system is the Advanced Micro Devices (AMD) 2900 series bit slice processor.

Central processing unit (CPU)

The CPU is the section of the processor in which the actual computation or logic operations are carried out. The CPU contains a number of storage registers, an arithmetic and logic unit (ALU) and an instruction decoder unit which also sets up the interconnections required to perform the requested instruction. The general arrangement is as shown in Figure 19.

The ALU is a logic array which can be programmed to perform a number of binary arithmetic operations such as addition and subtraction as well as logical operations such as AND, OR and EXCLUSIVE OR. Some more advanced microprocessors will also have the capability to carry out simple multiplication and division operations. The ALU normally has two inputs for the data which is to be operated upon and one output for the result.

In most processors a dedicated register, known as the accumulator, works in conjunction with the ALU in executing arithmetic or logical operations. As an example, for the addition of two numbers one of the numbers is initially placed in the accumulator register

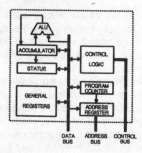

Figure 19 Block diagram of the central processor unit

and this feeds one of the inputs of the ALU. The second number is taken either from memory or from another CPU register and applied to the second ALU input. The result which appears at the output of the ALU is then transferred back into the accumulator.

Some of the more advanced 8-bit microprocessors have two accumulator registers which may be used separately or combined together to provide 16-bit arithmetic and logic operations. In the 16- and 32-bit processors there is usually a bank of general purpose registers any of which may be used with the ALU to perform some or all of the functions normally provided by an accumulator register.

All processors have a dedicated register known as the program counter (PC) which is used to hold the address of the next instruction to be processed. As each instruction is executed the PC register is automatically updated so that it contains the memory address for the memory location where the next instruction to be executed is stored.

The status register contains a number of flag bits which indicate various conditions that resulted from the execution of an instruction. As an example these bits will record whether the result was zero or negative. This register may also have bits indicating the state of the CPU such as, whether it is performing pure binary or BCD arithmetic, whether it will respond to interrupt inputs and in some types whether the CPU is in user or supervisor mode.

The other registers in the CPU may be generally classified as data or address registers. The data registers are used for temporarily holding data that is to be processed. Address registers are used to hold address information needed during the execution of some instructions. Examples of these are the index registers which allow the original address specified in an instruction to be modified by the contents of the index register. This is useful in handling arrays of data. Another dedicated address register is the stack pointer (SP) which contains the current address of a special area in memory known as the stack which is used to save the return address when handling subroutines and interrupts. In some processors any of the general purpose registers may be used either as data registers or address registers as required.

One register in the CPU which is not generally accessible to the programmer is the instruction register. This holds the operation code (opcode) of the instruction that is to be executed. Connected to the instruction register is a set of decoder logic which interprets the opcode and sets up the required links between registers and governs the sequence of actions to be carried out by the CPU in order to execute the instruction. The decoding logic is also linked to an address register which drives the address bus. Like the instruction register the address register itself is not directly accessible from the program but appropriate data will be transferred to it as an instruction is decoded and executed so that the correct memory locations are addressed for data transfers.

Data is transferred between the various units making up the computer system via a series of wires known as the bus system. Typically this is divided up into three groups of wires known as the data, address and control buses.

The data bus is used to transfer data between the CPU, memory and input–output ports. This bus system is bidirectional so that data can flow in either direction between the various units of the system. The direction of data flow is governed by signals on the control bus. The data is transferred across the data bus with one bit on each wire so that a complete data word is transferred in one operation. In microcomputer systems the number of bits in the data word transferred across the data bus is generally used to divide the systems into separate groups. Thus there are typically 4-bit, 8-bit, 16-bit and 32-bit microcomputer systems in current use.

In general, the 4-bit systems are normally used for dedicated microcontroller devices such as those used in domestic appliances. The 8-bit and 16-bit systems are generally used for personal computers and for industrial controllers whilst 32-bit systems are used for specialized purposes such as graphics workstations and minicomputers.

The address bus is an output from the microprocessor and is used to select memory locations or input–output devices and connect them with the data bus so that data can be transferred to or from the CPU. Most 8-bit processors such as the Z80 and 6502 have a 16-bit address bus which allows for 65,536 different address codes. Such a processor could access up to 64k bytes of memory although some of these addresses might be set aside to select input or output channels. On the Z80 it is possible to separately address up to 256 input or output channels without using memory addresses since for input and output instructions the lower 8-bits of the address bus may be used as a separate input or output (I/O) address bus.

Apart from the address and data bus systems there are also a number of control and status signals which link the CPU to the memory and I/O devices. These signals may generally be considered as control buses. One important control signal indicates which way data is to flow across the data bus. Signals coming from the CPU represent a write condition and when signals are to be fed into the CPU this is a read condition. Some processors, such as the 6502, 6800 and 68000, have a single read or write (R/W) control line whose state indicates whether a read or write operation is to take place. Other types, such as the 8085, Z80 and 8086, have separate read and write control lines.

The CPU also sends out various timing signals which govern the point at which data transfers take place across the data bus. In most processors a signal is output when the data on the address bus is valid and stable to ensure that data is transferred only when the memory location has been properly selected. Some processors provide an address strobe signal for this purpose. In processors such as the 68000 a handshake system may be used for the data bus. Here a data strobe signal from the CPU indicates that data can be transferred and a data acknowledge signal from the external device indicates that data has been transferred. This type of operation is important if the memory device operates more slowly than the CPU and the effect is to make the CPU wait for the slower device. In processors such as the Z80 and 8085 a WAIT signal generated by the memory system performs a similar function and the CPU idles until the WAIT signal is removed and then the data transfer takes place.

Normally the CPU controls the bus system but for some applications, such as direct memory access, or in multiprocessor systems another external device must be able to take over control of the bus system for a period of time. For this to happen the main CPU must relinquish control over the bus system and this is initiated by applying a bus request signal to the CPU. On receipt of this signal the CPU completes its current instruction and then releases control of the bus system by disconnecting itself from the address and data bus lines and some of the control lines such as R/W. When the bus is free a bus available signal is output from the CPU and the external device may then take control of the bus system. When the bus request signal is removed the CPU resumes its control of the bus system.

Solid state memories

An important part of any computer system is the memory which is used to hold the program instructions which the CPU will execute and the data which is to be processed as well as any results produced. The memory is effectively a large array of pigeonholes each of which contains one item or word of data.

The process of placing new data into the memory is called a write operation. When data held in the memory is examined this is called a read operation. Most memory devices permit both writing and reading operations and are referred to as read/write (R/W) memories. Some memories only permit the reading of stored data and are called read-only memories (ROMs).

Most memory devices are of the type where any individual location within the memory array can be directly selected for reading or writing. This type of memory is known as a random access memory (RAM). In practice the term RAM is usually used to describe a read/write RAM.

RAM devices may be classified as dynamic or static according to the way in which data is stored in the device. In a static memory the data state is held until a new write operation is made to the memory cell. Dynamic memory cells retain their data for a short time and must be 'refreshed' at regular intervals to ensure that the stored data is not lost. Refreshing involves reading the data from the cell and then writing it back in again.

Most electronic memory devices lose their stored data if the power supply is switched off and are referred to as volatile memories. Some types, however, have the data permanently built into the memory or retain the stored data even if the power supply is turned off and are referred to as non-volatile memories.

Dynamic memories

The simplest form of memory cell makes use of the charge storage property of a capacitor. A memory cell of this capacitive type could have the simple form shown in Figure 20. If switch S1 is closed the capacitor charges or discharges until the voltage across it is the same as that on the data input line. When S1 is opened the capacitor will theoretically retain its state of charge indefinitely. To read the data switch S2 is closed and the capacitor voltage level is fed to the output line via buffer amplifier. A practical memory cell consists of a small capacitor and some solid state switches which enable the capacitor to be selected and connected to the data input or output lines to allow data to be written into or read from the cell. Each memory cell of this type holds 1 bit of data.

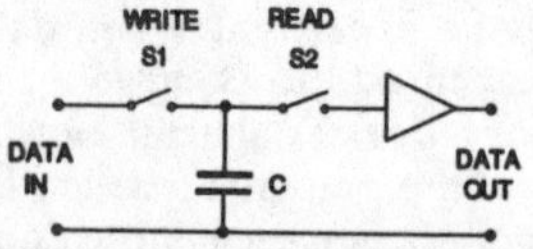

Figure 20 A simple memory cell using a capacitor

The capacitor in a memory cell is not, in fact, a perfect capacitor since there will be leakage paths through it and the switching circuits which will allow the charge to slowly leak away. The result is that after a period of time the data state stored in the capacitor will be lost. In a practical storage cell the time for which data can be held reliably is only a few milliseconds so some means of retaining the data must be employed if the cell is to be useful for a computer memory device.

The technique used to make a capacitor cell retain its data reliably is known as 'refreshing' and consists simply of reading the data from the cell at regular intervals and then writing it back into the cell. When the data is rewritten the capacitor is again recharged to its original state so that the data is refreshed and will be retained for a further period of time. In practical memory devices the refresh operation is usually carried out at intervals of about 2 to 4 ms.

Static memories

An alternative type of memory cell uses a flip-flop circuit which can be set to one or other of its stable states to represent either a 1 or a 0. Once set the flip-flop will hold its state until a new write operation is made and a memory made up of flip-flop cells will be a static type.

The disadvantage of the static type of memory cell is that the circuit of the cell is more complex than that of a dynamic type. Thus for a given size of silicon chip the capacity of a static memory will be less than that of a dynamic memory. On the other hand, static memories are generally much faster in operation and have the advantage that they do not require refresh circuits to maintain the data.

Memory addressing

The simplest way of selecting an individual cell in a memory array would be to have a separate select wire for each cell and to energize this line to select the particular cell which is to have data written to it or read from it. For a large memory with perhaps 500,000 cells this would be totally impractical.

The usual method employed for selecting individual cells in a memory array is to arrange the cells in an array of rows and columns. Now a single select wire can be used to select all of the cells in a particular column and a second select wire can select all of the cells in a particular row. Only one cell at the junction of the selected row and column will have both select inputs active and is selected for reading or writing. In such an array all of the data input lines of the cells are joined in parallel and the output lines are similarly wired together. Thus the selected cell is automatically connected to the input and output data lines.

A further reduction in the number of pins required on the memory chip is achieved by entering the row and column numbers as binary codes. Thus if the array consisted of thirty-two rows and thirty-two columns direct row and column selection would require sixty-four address lines. The numbers 0 to 31 can however be represented by a 5-bit binary number so if binary address inputs were used only ten address lines would be needed. The general arrangement would be as shown in Figure 21.

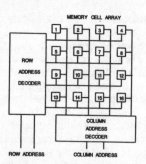

Figure 21 Addressing scheme for a memory cell array

Most dynamic memory devices use a multiplexed address input scheme to further reduce the number of pins needed for address inputs. Here the row address is applied first and when the address is stable a row address strobe (RAS) is applied. When RAS switches from 1 to 0 the address is latched into a row address register inside the memory chip. The column address is then applied to the address inputs and a column address strobe (CAS) is activated. When CAS goes to 0 the column address is latched into a second on chip register and the entire row-column address is then used to select the memory cell for the read or write operation.

A write enable control input to the memory chip determines the direction of data flow and this line is usually held low for a write operation. Some memory devices have separate lines for data input and output whilst others have a common data in/out pin and switching is carried out internally under the control of the write enable input.

Common dynamic RAM types

Early dynamic memory chips contained 4096 cells and are usually referred to as 4k bit memory chips. The next development was the 16,384 bit or 16k bit memory chip which was widely used in the 8-bit home computers. Further development allowed 65,536 bit or 64k bit memory chips to be made and these were soon followed by chips containing 256k bits of memory which are widely used in modern 16-bit personal computer systems. More recently chips containing 1M bit of memory have become available and experimental 4M bit dynamic memory devices have been produced and are likely to become common in a few years time.

Type	Organization	Package
4116	16k × 1 bit	16-pin DIL
4164	64k × 1 bit	16-pin DIL
4416	16k × 4 bit	18-pin DIL
41256	256k × 1 bit	16-pin DIL
4464	64k × 4 bits	18-pin DIL
511000	1024k × 1 bit	18-pin DIL

Figure 22 shows the pin connections for these dynamic memory types.

Common static RAM types

Static memory devices generally have smaller capacities than dynamic types but have the advantage of higher speed and no need for refresh circuits. Typical sizes for static RAM chips are 1k, 4k, 16k and 64k bits. Whereas most of the popular dynamic memories consist of a single bit plane the static types are often arranged with 4- or 8-bit planes so that complete data words can be transferred at a time. Typical arrangements are 1k × 4-bits, 2k × 8-bits and 8k × 8-bits.

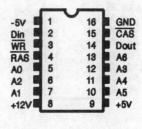

4116

(a)

continued

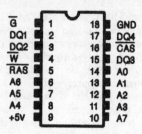

4416

(b)

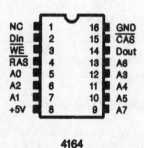

4164

(c)

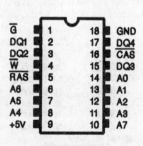

4464

(d)

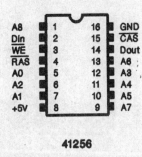

41256

(e)

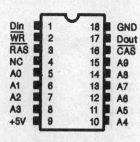

511000

Figure 22 Pin connections of typical dynamic RAM chips

Type	Organization	Technology
2114	1k × 4-bit	NMOS
4801-4	1k × 8-bit	NMOS
6116-3	2k × 8-bit	CMOS
6264	8k × 8-bit	CMOS
62256	32k × 8-bit	CMOS

Figure 23 shows the pin connections for these static RAM types.

Read-only memories (ROMs)

Read-only memories fall into two major groups known as mask programmed and field programmable. The mask programmed memories have their data built into them when they are manufactured and cannot be altered. These are used for mass produc-

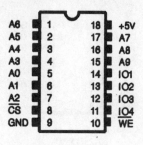

2114

(a)

4801-4

(b)

6116

(c)

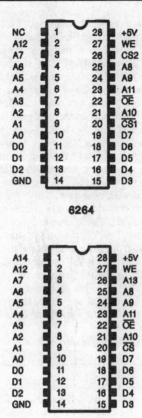

NC	1	28	+5V
A12	2	27	WE
A7	3	26	CS2
A6	4	25	A8
A5	5	24	A9
A4	6	23	A11
A3	7	22	$\overline{OE}$
A2	8	21	A10
A1	9	20	$\overline{CS1}$
A0	10	19	D7
D0	11	18	D6
D1	12	17	D5
D2	13	16	D4
GND	14	15	D3

6264

(d)

A14	1	28	+5V
A12	2	27	WE
A7	3	26	A13
A6	4	25	A8
A5	5	24	A9
A4	6	23	A11
A3	7	22	$\overline{OE}$
A2	8	21	A10
A1	9	20	$\overline{CS}$
A0	10	19	D7
D0	11	18	D6
D1	12	17	D5
D2	13	16	D4
GND	14	15	D3

62256

(e)

Figure 23 Pin connections of typical static RAM chips

tion of standard pattern memories such as character generator ROMs.

Field programmable memories may be of the fusible link type where all cells are initially set to the same state. To program the data into the memory a series of wire links inside the ROM are fused to change the data state of individual cells. This is done by addressing individual cells and passing a pulse of current through the cell to fuse its wire link and change its logic state. Once altered the data in a cell cannot be changed again. These types are called programmable read only memories (PROMs).

An alternative form of PROM has memory cells in which data is stored as a charge in much the same way as in a dynamic RAM cell. In these devices, however, the stored charge can be held for many years. Programming is done by selecting individual cells and applying both the data signal and a large voltage pulse which sets up the charge in the cell. The chip package has a quartz window over the actual memory chip. By shining high energy ultraviolet light on to the chip via the quartz window the charge in each memory cell is dissipated and the entire memory is erased. Once erased the memory can be reprogrammed with new data. This type of ROM is known as an erasable programmable read-only memory (EPROM). These are particularly useful for development work where the program or data needs to be changed from time to time.

Another variation on the programmable ROM is the electrically erasable programmable read-only memory (EEPROM). This is similar to an EPROM but the erasure is carried out by applying an electrical signal rather than using ultraviolet light.

Ultraviolet erasable PROM types

Type	Organization	Package
2758	1k × 8-bit	24-pin DIL
2716	2k × 8-bit	24-pin DIL
2732	4k × 8-bit	28-pin DIL
2764	8k × 8-bit	28-pin DIL
27128	16k × 8-bit	28-pin DIL
27256	32k × 8-bit	28-pin DIL
27512	64k × 8-bit	28-pin DIL

The pin connections of these popular EPROM types are shown in Figure 24.

Magnetic disk memories

The most popular form of mass data storage for personal and small business computers is the floppy disk in one of its various forms. The recording medium consists of a thin flexible plastic disk coated on both sides with a magnetic oxide layer. Data is recorded on a series of concentric circular tracks by

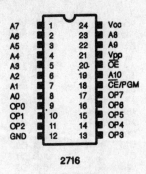

(a)

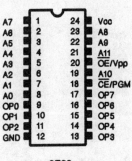

(b)

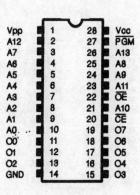

(c)

continued

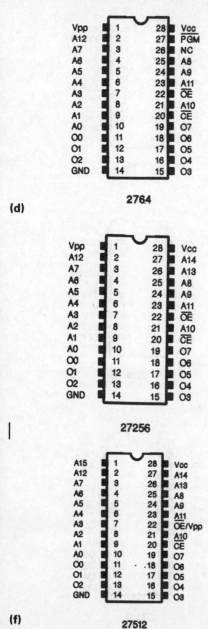

(d)

2764

27256

(f)

27512

Figure 24 Pin connections of typical EPROM chips

magnetizing the oxide layer using a head similar to that on an audio cassette recorder. The head is mounted on a movable arm so that it can be positioned over any desired track on the disk. As the disk rotates under the head pulses are applied to coils on the head to produce a series of magnetic pulses on the disk track.

Early versions of floppy disks used an 8 inch diameter disk mounted in a flexible protective envelope. These are generally referred to as standard floppy disks but are not often used today. A smaller minifloppy was then introduced where the disk was 5.25 inches in diameter. By using improved recording techniques and more accurate disk drive mechanisms it became possible to provide at least as much memory capacity on the smaller disk as on the earlier 8 inch version. More recently two smaller formats for floppy disks have been introduced. The 3.5 inch microfloppy disk has a hard plastic protective case and is generally more robust than the 5.25 inch disk. Again owing due to improved recording techniques and drive mechanics the 3.5 inch disk can provide the same or better capacity than a 5.25 inch type. An even smaller 3 inch compact floppy disk introduced by Hitachi is also available. This type of disk also has a hard plastic case but is only used by a few computer makers since the 3.5 inch has become established as the more popular standard.

Disks may be recorded with either 40 or 80 tracks across the surface of the disk. Most systems use the 80 track format in order to achieve a higher memory capacity. Some disk drives are designed to record on both sides of the disk thus giving twice the data capacity. Early systems used a simple recording format known as single density recording. Most modern disk systems use a modified scheme giving double density recording and again doubling the capacity of a given disk.

Each track is divided into a number of blocks of data called sectors. In a typical system data is written or read one sector at a time. A complete data record on a disk is called a file and may consist of any integer number of sectors of data.

Standard floppy disk

This type of magnetic storage disk was first introduced by IBM for their data entry systems. The outer envelope is 8 inches square and contains a flexible plastic magnetic coated disk. A slot in each side of the disk envelope allows the head to make contact with the magnetic coating to allow reading or writing of data. A hole in the centre of the disk and envelope allows the drive unit to rotate the magnetic disk inside the envelope. At a point close to this central drive hole there is a small index hole which is used with a photocell and lamp in the drive unit to give a pulse once per revolution of the disk. This gives a reference point to indicate the first sector on each track. A notch in one edge of the envelope is used to write protect the disk if desired.

There are 77 track positions per side on these disks. Allowing for the possibility of up to two bad tracks there are normally 75 usable tracks available on a single sided disk with 150 tracks for a double sided disk.

Standard sector formats for 8 inch disks are

8 sectors $\times$ 512 bytes = 4096 bytes per track
15 sectors $\times$ 256 bytes = 3840 bytes per track
26 sectors $\times$ 128 bytes = 3328 bytes per track

Single-sided disks give a typical capacity of 250k bytes whilst a double-sided disk provides 500k bytes of storage.

This type of disk is now obsolete since most systems have adopted the smaller mini- and microfloppy formats.

Minifloppy disk

This form of disk storage, also known as a mini diskette, is similar in construction to the 8 inch floppy disk but uses an envelope which is 5.25 inches square. A band approximately 1 inch wide and near the outer edge of the disk is used for recording. Like the standard floppy disk the 5.25 inch version has an index hole and a write protect notch.

The disk may be recorded with 40 tracks at a spacing of 48 tracks per inch or 80 tracks at a spacing of 96 tracks per inch. Some computers such as the Apple II use only 35 tracks per side but the track pitch is the same as for 40 tracks.

Two forms of 5.25 inch disk were originally produced. One known as a hard sectored disk had 16 index holes in the disk which located the start of individual sectors on the track as well as the normal index hole to identify the first sector. The second type was the soft sectored disk where the individual sectors are identified by data recorded in a sector header block at the start of each sector. All modern 5.25 inch disk systems now use the soft sectored type of disk.

The usual sector format is 16 sectors with either 256 or 512 bytes per sector. Older versions of the Apple computers used a 13 sector format with 256 bytes per sector. Disks with 512 byte sectors use the double density modified frequency modulation (MFM) recording system. Older types of disk drive were only designed to cope with 40 tracks per side but modern drives are designed for 80 track operation and can be switched to operate in the 40 track format if desired. Many drives can also be switched to operate with either frequency modulation (FM) or MFM recording so that they can operate in either single or double density mode.

Minifloppy disks are tested after manufacture and graded for single or double density and single- or double-sided use. The typical unformatted capacities for such disks using an 80 track format are:

Single-side single density (SSSD)   250k bytes
Single-side double density (SSDD)   500k bytes
Double-side single density (DSSD)   500k bytes
Double-side double density (DSDD)   1M byte

With a 40 track format the capacity is halved to give a range from 125k bytes up to 500k bytes.

Microfloppy disk

This floppy disk format was developed by Sony and uses a 3.5 inch wide by 3.625 inch long package. Unlike the larger floppy disks the envelope is made of hard rigid plastic and also incorporates a metal shutter which protects the disk surface when the disk is removed from the drive. At one end of the disk case is a hole with a movable cover which is used to provide write protection for the disk. Location notches in the disk prevent it from being inserted incorrectly in the drive.

The standard track pitch for 3.5 inch microfloppy disks is 135 tracks per inch with 80 tracks on each side of the disk. Some drives support a 40 track layout with a pitch of 67.5 tracks per inch. Most systems in fact use the 80 track format.

Typical sector formats for the 3.5 inch disk are:

9 sectors × 1024 bytes = 4.5k bytes per track
10 sectors × 1024 bytes = 5k bytes per track

This provides an unformatted capacity of about 500k bytes for a single sided disk and 1M byte for a double sided disk. All disks of this type use the MFM recording technique. When the disk is formatted the available space for data is reduced to about 360k bytes for a 9 sector/track format and 400k bytes when 10 sectors are used per track.

Compact floppy disk

This format was developed by Hitachi as a competitor to the Sony 3.5 inch disk. It uses a disk of about 3 inches in diameter in a hard case some 3.125 inches wide by 4 inches long. Like the 3.5 inch disk it has a hard plastic cover and a metal shutter protects the magnetic disk when it is removed from the drive. The disk provides a typical capacity of some 700k bytes unformatted using 80 tracks double-sided with MFM recording. This type of disk is turned upside down in the drive to access the second side.

This format has been used by a few manufacturers, such as Amstrad for their personal computers, but has not been widely accepted and will probably tend to be replaced by the 3.5 inch format in future systems.

Single density (FM) recording format

For single density recording a technique known as frequency modulation (FM) is used. Each bit period or cell is divided into four equal time slots as shown in Figure 25. The first contains a clock pulse and is followed by a zero level signal in the second period. The third period reflects the bit state (1 or 0) and the fourth is a zero (0). Thus when a bit is at the 1 state its cell contains two pulses whilst a 0 state contains only one pulse. The first pulse in a bit cell is used as a clock and the second carries the data.

An advantage of this format is that the built in clock pulse makes decoding fairly straightforward. The main disadvantage is that the clock pulse conveys no useful information.

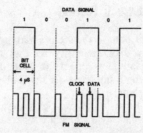

Figure 25   The FM format for magnetic recording of data

Double density (MFM) recording format

For double density recording an alternative technique known as modified frequency modulation (MFM) is used. In this system only one pulse is written in a bit cell. If the data is a 1 then a pulse is written at the centre of the bit cell whilst for a 0 no pulse is written. In order to maintain the clock timing however when a pair of 0 bits follow one another a clock pulse is written at the start of the cell containing the second 0 as shown in Figure 26. The advantage of this method of recording is that with the same bit cell length the data rate can be doubled. Decoding is a little more complex than for FM but this system is now widely used to give higher data density on floppy disks.

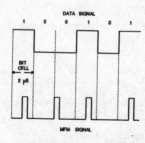

Figure 26   The MFM format for magnetic recording of data

Sector and track format

The layout of data in the sectors making up a track on a floppy disk generally follows the format originally adopted in the IBM 3740 disk format except that the number of sectors and their length may be different.

Each sector consists of two fields known as the ID field and the data field which are separated by an ID gap. Following the data field is a further gap known as the data gap which separates the sector from the next sector on the track as shown in Figure 27.

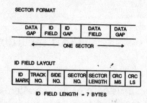

Figure 27 Typical layout of a sector on a magnetic disk

ID field format

The ID field consists of 7 bytes of information. This starts with an ID address mark byte. The second byte shows the number of track and this is followed by a sector number byte. The fifth byte indicates the sector length coded as follows:

Sector length bytes	Byte value
128	00
256	01
512	02
1024	03

The last two bytes of this field provide a cyclic redundancy check (CRC) for error detection.

Data field format

This field starts with a data address mark then continues with the sector data and is completed by a pair of bytes as the CRC for error checking. The length of the data section is 128, 256, 512 or 1024 bytes as specified by the ID field.

Inter field gaps

Between each sector and the next there is a data gap which consists of a fixed pattern of bits to facilitate clock synchronization. Within each sector there is also an ID gap between the end of the ID field and the start of the data field. After the last sector on the track there is a pre-index gap which is somewhat longer than the other gaps. A further gap exists between the index hole position and the start of the first sector. This is known as the post-index gap. The main function of these gaps is to allow for tolerances in the rotation speed and read/write circuit timing between different disk drives.

Disk formatting

Normally a new disk is totally blank and the first requirement before it can be used is that it must be formatted. During this process the sector ID and data fields are written on to each track of the disk according to the format requirements of the computer system being used.

Apart from writing the sector information the formatting program will also write data into some tracks of the disk. Usually the system will reserve one or more tracks for use as a directory which will keep a record of files as they are written to the disk. In most systems there will also be a file allocation table which keeps a record of all the sectors that are used and which files they belong to. One sector, usually the first on track 0, is used as a boot sector. This sector is read when the computer is started or reset and may allow the computer to automatically run a specific program from the disk. On some systems the boot sector is read every time a new disk is accessed.

Hard disks

To obtain very large amounts of mass memory many personal computer systems now use Winchester type hard disk systems. In this type of unit a rigid metal disk is used and this is generally mounted in a sealed unit to exclude dust. The disk heads float just above the surface of the disk unlike the normal floppy disk head which runs in contact with the disk surface.

In a hard disk the speed of rotation can be much higher than for a floppy disk and it is possible to greatly increase both the number of tracks and the recording density along the track. Thus a 5.25 inch Winchester type unit with a single disk can have a capacity of perhaps 5M bytes with a very much higher data transfer speed than the equivalent floppy disk unit. Larger disk capacities can be achieved by stacking several disks on the same drive shaft with separate read/write heads for each disk. In this way hard disk drives of 20, 30, 40 and 60M bytes can readily be produced. Some hard disk units now use a 3.5 inch diameter disk to provide an even more compact unit.

One disadvantage of the Winchester type unit is that the disk is sealed in and cannot therefore be changed in the same way as a floppy disk can. To avoid possible loss of vast amounts of data in the event of failure of the hard disk unit it is usual to save the entire contents of the hard disk at regular intervals by copying them to either a cartridge tape or to a set of floppy disks. The major advantage is that a vast amount of data can be accessed very rapidly and this can be particularly useful in database type applications.

4 Instruction sets

The operations inside a microprocessor CPU are governed by instructions read from the program memory. These normally consists of an opcode which defines the type of operation to be carried out and for many instructions there is also an operand which generally indicates the address to be accessed in the main memory. The operand is normally held in one or two memory locations immediately following the opcode. Operations between or on registers inside the CPU are generally defined within the opcode itself so there is no operand and the instruction takes up only one word in memory.

During the execution of an instruction the CPU will first read the opcode from the memory and this is then decoded inside the CPU. After decoding the CPU may then make further data transfers from memory to obtain the operand and finally it will execute the instruction itself which may involve a further data transfer to or from memory.

Data transfer instructions

A commonly used instruction in microprocessor systems is the data transfer operation. This may involve movement of a word of data from, say, the external memory to a CPU register such as the accumulator. This is usually accomplished by a LOAD instruction which may be written as LDA for loading accumulator A or, say, LDX for loading data from memory into register X.

The reverse operation where data is transferred from a register to memory is generally called a STORE instruction and is often abbreviated to the form STA, STB, STX etc.

Some processors use the instruction MOVE to perform data transfer operations and this is usually followed by two addresses which indicate the source and the destination of the data. This MOVE A, ADDR would tell the processor to store the data in register A in the memory location given by the address ADDR.

For Motorola and Zilog processors the format is usually MOVE s,d where s is the source address from which data is to be taken and d is the destination address where the data is to be placed. Intel uses the reverse arrangement so the instruction takes the form MOV d,s.

Data may be transferred between the internal registers of the CPU. Many processors use special instructions for this type of data transfer operation. As an example, the 6502 processor uses the instruction TAX to transfer the contents of the accumulator A to the X index register. Other processors use a MOVE instruction so that for a 68000 CPU the instruction MOVE D0,A7 would copy the contents of register D0 into register A7.

Generally, for data transfer instructions the data held in the source location is not altered by the instruction but the destination location is overwritten with new data.

In 8-bit processors the data transfer moves a byte of data at a time although some processors have instructions which will move a 16-bit word using one instruction. Such an instruction would cause the CPU to access the memory twice to load the two 8-bit bytes. Some processors such as the Intel 8088 have 16-bit internal registers but only an 8-bit bus. Here again the CPU will make two memory data transfers during the execution of the instruction. The 16- and 32-bit processors generally have instructions in which either a byte, a 16-bit word or a 32-bit double word can be transferred in one operation.

Arithmetic operations

To carry out addition of two binary numbers pairs of bits, one from each number, are added together starting with the least significant bit (LSB). Suppose we have a pair of bits with bit A coming from one number and bit B from the second. The four possible results of adding the two bits together are shown in Figure 28.

BIT A	BIT B	SUM	CARRY
0	0	0	0
1	0	1	0
0	1	1	0
1	1	0	1

Figure 28 Truth table for adding two binary data bits

When one or other of the input bits is at 1 the sum will be a bit set at 1. When both bits A and B are at 1 the sum has the value 2. In this case the sum bit is set at 0 and a carry is produced to the next higher order bit in the result. For addition of the higher order bits, therefore, any carry from the next lower bit position must be taken into account. This gives a total of eight possible results from the addition of the two input bits and any carry from the next lower bit as shown in Figure 29.

BIT A	BIT B	CARRY IN	SUM	CARRY OUT
0	0	0	0	0
1	0	0	1	0
0	1	0	1	0
1	1	0	0	1
0	0	1	1	0
1	0	1	0	1
0	1	1	0	1
1	1	1	1	1

Figure 29 Truth table for add with carry operation

This entire function of add with carry can be implemented using a set of simple logic gates for each bit position of the numbers being added. Thus for adding two 8-bit words a set of eight adder circuits would be used with the carry signals linked from one bit position to the next. Now by applying two 8-bit numbers A and B to the adder network the sum will appear at the 8 output lines together with any carry bit output produced by adding the most significant bits of numbers A and B.

Binary subtraction follows a similar logic process and the 8 possible results of subtracting bit B from bit A are shown in Figure 30.

BIT A	BIT B	CARRY IN	DIFF A - B	CARRY OUT
0	0	0	0	0
1	0	0	1	0
0	1	0	1	1
1	1	0	0	0
0	0	1	1	1
1	0	1	0	0
0	1	1	0	1
1	1	1	1	1

Figure 30 Truth table for subtract with carry operation

Here the carry in bit represents a borrow made by the calculation of the next lower bit and the carry out is a borrow from the next higher bit. This subtraction function between the bits of two binary words can be carried out by an array of simple logic gates in much the same way as addition and when words A and B are applied at the inputs of the subtractor logic network the resultant difference and any carry bit will appear at the output.

All microprocessors have an ADD instruction which allows two numbers to be added together. The logic functions of addition and subtraction are implemented in an arithmetic and logic unit (ALU) within the CPU. One of the numbers has to be loaded into the accumulator before the ADD instruction is executed. The operand of the ADD instruction provides the memory address for the second number which is then added or subtracted and the result is placed in the accumulator. Most 16- and 32-bit processors allow several of their internal registers to be used as accumulators for such arithmetic operations.

Processors usually perform binary addition using complementary arithmetic to allow negative numbers to be handled. If the result is too large to be held in the accumulator a carry is produced and this is generally held in a carry flag bit in the CPU status register. The simple ADD instruction assumes that there is no input carry.

Most types of microprocessor have an alternative ADD with carry (ADC) instruction which takes into account any previous carry when the addition is carried out. In this case the carry flag bit in the status register provides the input carry signal for the LSB of the calculation. This instruction is used when two 16-bit numbers are to be added in an 8-bit CPU. First the lower 8-bits of the two numbers are added together and the result is stored in memory. Storing and loading operations do not affect the carry flag so when the most significant 8-bits are added the carry from the previous addition can be added in to give the correct answer. Larger numbers can be handled by a succession of ADC operations in which the carry is taken into account for the more significant bytes.

Some types of microprocessor, such as the 6502, only have ADC type instructions. In this case for a simple ADD operation it is important that the carry bit should be cleared before the ADC instruction is executed otherwise a carry bit produced by some previous instruction could be added in to give an incorrect result.

Most processors provide a subtract (SUB) instruction which will subtract a number from the contents of the accumulator and leave the result in the accumulator. In the subtract operation a borrow may be required and this is signified by setting the carry bit in the status register. A subtract with carry (SBC) or subtract with borrow (SBB) instruction is usually provided which allows large numbers to be dealt with in several segments in a similar fashion to the use of the ADC instruction. The 6502 only has an SBC instruction and with this CPU it is important to set the carry bit to 1 if a simple subtract without carry operation is required.

Processors usually have facilities for adding numbers in BCD format. In some cases a different form of ADD instruction is used which automatically corrects for the BCD format. In other cases the normal binary ADD or ADC operation is used and then a decimal add adjust (DAA) instruction is executed which modifies the binary result to produce the correct BCD sum. Subtraction using the BCD format may either have a special subtract instruction or be carried out by using binary subtraction and a decimal adjust instruction to correct the result.

Some processors do not have a subtract instruction at all but do have a negate (NEG) instruction which effectively subtracts the data from zero thus changing its sign. This negated number can now be added to a second number and the result is the same as if the first number had been subtracted.

Multiplication is a rather more complex operation which involves a series of successive additions. It can be carried out by a fairly simple software routine. The result of the multiplication can have up to twice the number of bits that are in the numbers being multiplied. Thus multiplying two 8-bit numbers together will give a 16-bit result.

For multiplication by powers of two a simple shift left operation can be used since a single left shift is the same as multiplying the number by two. Two left shifts in succession represents ×4 and so on. For correct results any carry bits from the MSB end of the register must be shifted left into an extra register to provide the most significant part of the product.

A general multiplication routine examines each bit

of the multiplier in turn starting with the LSB. If the bit is a 1 the multiplicand is added to the MSB of the product register and then the product register is shifted 1 bit to the right. When the multiplier bit is a 0 only the shift of the product register is carried out. If the multiplier is an 8-bit number this operation is repeated eight times and at the end the product is contained in the product register. Note that the product always needs twice as many bits as the multiplier or multiplicand.

The 16- and 32-bit processors usually provide an integer multiply instruction which may be specified for either unsigned or signed numbers. Such an instruction usually causes the same basic routine to be executed within the CPU and multiplication will typically be somewhat slower to execute than a simple addition.

Division by powers of two can be achieved by simply carrying out right shift operations. One right shift represents divide by 2 and successive shifts will give divide by 4, 8, 16 and so on. One point to note here is that any fractional result is rounded off since the bits shifted out of the end of the register are lost.

Division by any integer number is a little more complex and involves successive subtractions. Here the divisor is subtracted from the dividend and if the result is positive a 1 is placed in the LSB of the quotient. If the result is negative the divisor is added in again to restore the dividend and a 0 is placed in the LSB of the quotient register. The quotient register contents are then shifted left by 1 bit and the dividend remainder is also shifted left by 1 bit. The sequence then continues for the number of bits in the original two numbers. Thus for two 8-bit numbers there will be eight subtract and shift operations.

The 16- and 32-bit processors usually provide signed and unsigned division instructions. For 8-bit processors a software routine is required.

Before carrying out a division it is important to check if the divisor is zero since this should theoretically produce an infinite result. In a software routine this needs to be detected and signalled to the user otherwise an incorrect result will be produced. Processors with a divide instruction will usually generate an interrupt or trap operation when a divide by zero condition is detected.

Floating point arithmetic

Arithmetic using the floating point format follows different rules from the simple integer arithmetic. When adding or subtracting numbers the scaling must be changed so that the two exponents are the same. In the case of a base ten system if the exponent is increased by 1 the mantissa value must be divided by 10 to keep the data value the same. Once the exponents are the same the two mantissa values are added together or subtracted.

For multiplication the exponents are added together to give the new value for the exponent of the result. The mantissa values are then multiplied together to give the new mantissa. In the case of division the divisor exponent is subtracted from that of the dividend. The mantissa parts of the data are divided in the normal way.

After each floating point operation the data is usually normalized to give the best precision. This involves adjusting the exponent and mantissa until the mantissa has its largest permissible value. If the result of an addition causes a mantissa greater than 1 then the exponent is incremented and the mantissa reduced to bring it within its permissible range.

Logical operations

All processors provide a range of logical operations which can be carried out on the data held in the accumulator. The usual functions provided are AND, OR, and EXCLUSIVE OR. These functions operate on individual bits in the data word. A further function that is generally provided is the NOT or INVERT operation which changes the state of all of the bits in the data word.

Shift operations involve moving the pattern of bits in the register one place to the right or left. The usual shift functions are logic shift right (LSR) in which a 0 is shifted into the most significant bit and the previous least significant bit is moved to the carry flag in the status register as shown in Figure 31. For a logic shift left (LSL) the 0 is shifted into the LS bit and the old MSB is moved to the carry flag as shown in Figure 32.

An alternative version of the shift operation is the arithmetic shift. For arithmetic shift right (ASR) the action is as shown in Figure 33. Here the MSB is

Figure 31 Data movement for logic shift right (LSR)

Figure 32 Data movement for logic shift left (LSL)

copied so that it remains as it was before the shift and the LSB is shifted out to the carry flag. This arrangement ensures that when a signed number is shifted it retains its correct sign. The action of arithmetic shift left (ASL) is the same as logic shift left.

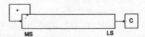

Figure 33 Data movement for arithmetic shift right (ASR)

A variation of the shift operation is rotation. For rotate right (ROR) the data word is shifted 1 bit to the right and the bit that spills out at the LS end is written back into the MSB position so that data circulates around the register as shown in Figure 34. Rotate left (ROL) causes data to circulate around the register in the opposite direction as shown in Figure 35 with the original MSB being written into the LSB position. In each of these operations the bit that moves out of the end of the register may also be copied into the carry flag. These rotation operations are useful for examining a word one bit at a time without losing the original data word.

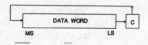

Figure 34 Data movement for rotate right (ROR)

Figure 35 Data movement for rotate left (ROL)

An alternative variation of the rotate operation moves the data word through the carry bit. Here the rotate right via carry (RORC) operation causes the old LSB to move to the carry and the old carry state to be moved into the MSB position as shown in Figure 36. The effect of this is that to restore the word to its initial state the number of rotate operations is one more than the number of bits in the word. Rotate left via carry is shown in Figure 37. In the Motorola 68000 these operations are called ROXR or ROXL and an extension X bit is used in the rotation loop to hold the bit which spills from the register. In the 6800 and 6500 processors the ordinary ROR and ROL operations are carried out via the carry flag.

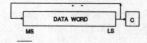

Figure 36 Data movement for rotate right via carry (RORC)

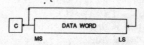

Figure 37 Data movement for rotate left via carry (ROLC)

Test and branch operations

One very important facility in any microprocessor system is the ability to choose one of a number of different sequences of program operation according to the state of a variable. This is achieved by using various test functions combined with branch or jump instructions which send the program execution to a specified instruction in the program sequence.

As an instruction is executed the processor will generally test the resultant data and set up one or more flag bits in the CPU status register. The usual flag bits provided are:

Z flag Indicates that the data is zero (All bits = 0)
N flag Indicates a negative number (MSB set at 1)
C flag Indicates that a carry occurred
V flag Indicates an arithmetic overflow

Arithmetic overflow occurs when the result in the accumulator is outside the range of numbers that can be represented by the data word. Some instructions, such as STORE, do not cause the status flag bits to be affected at all whilst others may affect only one or two of the status flags. The detailed instruction set for a particular CPU will usually indicate which status bits are affected by each type of instruction.

A conditional branch instruction is one which examines the status bits and when a specified condition is met the program branches to a new point in the program sequence which is specified by the address of the branch instruction. If the specified condition is not met the program continues normally with the next instruction following the branch instruction.

Most processors provide BEQ (branch if equal to zero) and BNE (branch if not zero) and these are governed by the state of the Z bit in the status register. Other branch opertions commonly provided and the status bits they use are as follows:

BCC	Branch if carry clear	C bit = 0
BCS	Branch if carry set	C bit = 1
BMI	Branch if minus	N bit = 1
BPL	Branch if plus	N bit = 0
BVS	Branch if overflow set	V bit = 1
BVC	Branch if overflow clear	V bit = 0

For branch instructions the relative addressing mode is used where the address is measured relative to the current program counter value. The operand of the branch instruction is called the offset and this is added to the value of the program counter to produce the effective address for the next instruction opcode.

Some processors provide a series of conditional jump instructions where the address can be specified either absolutely or indirectly.

Subroutines

In a program there are many short sequences of instructions which are used frequently throughout the main program. The appropriate sections of code could of course be repeated many times in the main program but a more convenient technique is to use a subroutine.

To call the subroutine from the main program a

special instruction is used. This may be either BSR (branch to subroutine), JSR (jump to subroutine) or, for some processors, it may be simply CALL.

When the subroutine branch or call instruction is executed the contents of the program counter are saved and the address operand of the subroutine call instruction is placed in the program counter. This address is that of the first instruction in the subroutine code. Thus execution now jumps to the subroutine. At the end of the subroutine there is another special instruction which may be either RET (return) or RTS (return from subroutine). The effect of this instruction is to cause the saved PC value from the main program to be restored to the program counter so that execution of the main program resumes at the instruction after the subroutine call.

The advantage of using subroutines is that the subroutine code need only be written once in the memory yet it can be executed many times during the execution of the main program.

In simple processors a save register is used to hold the original PC data whilst the subroutine is executed and this data is transferred back to the PC when the return instruction is executed. General-purpose processors normally save the PC value to a stack in memory whilst a subroutine is executed.

The stack is a section of memory which acts as a first in last out memory. It acts in much the same way as, say, a pile of cards where only the top card can be moved. Thus if a card is added to the pile it becomes the new top card and will be the first to be taken off the pile.

The address of the top word of the stack is held in a register known as the stack pointer (SP). When a word is written to the stack the SP is adjusted to point to the address of the next free location in the stack memory. When a word is read from the stack the SP is first adjusted to point to the last word written to the stack and then the word is read out.

Data can also be placed on the stack by using a PUSH instruction. Data on the stack can be read back into a CPU register by using a PULL or POP instruction depending on whose processor you are using.

Most microprocessors write their stacks so that they build downwards in memory. Thus each time a word is written to the stack the SP is decremented by one to point to the new top of the stack position.

When subroutines are called the process of saving the program counter is automatic when the BSR or CALL instruction is executed. When interrupts are used the interrupt sequence will usually cause at least the PC and the status registers to be saved. Some processors such as the 6800 save all of the CPU registers to the stack automatically when an interrupt occurs.

Addressing modes

There are many addressing techniques or modes by which data can be transferred to or from the internal registers of the CPU.

Implied address

The simplest form of addressing is the implied address in which the address is defined by the instruction opcode itself and there is no operand. An example of this might be the instruction CLR A which sets the accumulator to zero. In many processors data transfers between internal registers and operations on data within them use this mode of addressing.

Immediate address

One simple form of addressing which is used for loading a constant value into a register is the Immediate mode of addressing. In this mode the byte in the memory location immediately following the instruction opcode is the constant to be loaded as shown below:

Memory address	Contents	
100	LDA	load instruction
101	5	constant to be loaded
102	Next opcode	

This mode of addressing may also be used for addition and subtraction of constants. This mode of addressing is usually indicated in the assembly language instruction by writing a # sign in front of the operand.

Absolute address

The most common method of addressing data in the memory is to use absolute addressing in which the full address of the data to be acted upon follows the opcode of the instruction. Thus the layout of an absolute addressed load instruction would be:

Memory address	Contents
100	LDA load instruction
101	Address (MSB)
102	Address (LSB)
103	—

Here the 16-bit word in locations 101 and 102 gives the address from which data is to be transferred to the accumulator. This same mode of addressing can also be used with a store instruction to write data into the memory.

When the instruction is executed the opcode is first read in and decoded, then two further memory read cycles are made to transfer the address data from the memory to the CPU address register. The new address is now placed on the address bus and the data transfer from memory to the accumulator occurs.

Zero page address

One disadvantage of absolute addressing is that for an 8-bit CPU 2 bytes of address data have to be read in after the opcode so that the instruction takes at least three machine cycles for execution. If the data to be transferred is in the lowest 256 bytes of memory then an 8-bit address is all that needs to be transferred since the upper 8 bits are all 0s. Some processors such as the 6800 and 6502 have a special page zero address mode which uses only a 1-byte address operand and automatically sets the upper 8 address bits at 0. The advantage of this address mode is that it takes only two machine cycles for execution thus speeding up operation of the program and also using less memory for storing the program.

In the 6809 a more advanced form of paged addressing is provided. This CPU has a page register into which can be written the upper 8 bits of the address for the memory page which is currently being used. Now if a page addressed instruction is executed it will take the upper 8 bits of the address from the page register thus allowing the use of the shortened address mode at any point in the memory map.

Relative address

When a branch instruction is executed the address to which the program jumps is calculated relative to the current value of the program counter. This is known as relative addressing. The address operand in this case is referred to as the offset. The effective address is produced by adding the offset to the contents of the program counter.

In this form of addressing it should be remembered that the PC will be pointing to the address of the next instruction opcode when the offset is added and this must be taken into account when calculating the offset. In practice an assembler program will usually allow the instruction to which the branch is to be made to be labelled. In the mnemonic code the label is inserted as the offset and the assembler automatically calculates the correct number to insert for the offset. It should be noted that the offset may be either positive or negative so that the branch can be either forwards or backwards from the current position in the program sequence.

Indexed address

A form of addressing that is useful for dealing with tables of values in the memory is known as indexed addressing. In this type of addressing the contents of a special register, known as the index register, are added to the address operand of the instruction to produce the effective address that is used by the instruction. By altering the value in the index register the address can be modified to point to different locations in memory. To access values in a table stored in consecutive locations in memory the address operand would be set to point to the memory location of the first item in the table. Setting the index register to zero allows the first item to be accessed. Incrementing the index register will allow successive items to be accessed in turn.

An example of a piece of program to read ten successive memory locations starting at location ADDR and print them out might be as follows:

```
        LDX #0          Set index at 0
LOOP LDA ADDR,X  Load data from ADDR + X
        JSR PRINT       Subroutine to print data
        INX             Increment value of X
        CPX #10         Is X = 10 ?
        BNE LOOP        No Repeat loop
        ...             Yes continue program
```

Some processors provide instructions which include automatic incrementing or decrementing of the index register. An example of this is the 68000 which could use one of the following MOVE instructions:

```
MOVE  D0, (A1)+
MOVE  D0, −(A1)
```

In the first case the address stored in register A1 provides the memory address to which the contents of register D0 are written and the value of A1 is automatically incremented after the data transfer takes place. In the second case the value in A1 is first decremented and then this is used as the address to which the contents of D0 are written. These operations are known as postincrement and predecrement indexed addressing.

Indirect address

Another very useful form of addressing is indirect addressing where the effective address used by the instruction is read from a memory location specified by the instruction operand. An example might be as follows:

```
LDA  (ADDR)
```

This says use the contents of the memory at address ADDR as the effective address from which data is to be loaded into the accumulator.

The advantage of this type of addressing is that the actual addresses used can be altered whilst the program is executing whereas the normal absolute address mode is fixed when the program is written.

An alternative form of indirect addressing has the address of the location to be accessed held in a register within the CPU.

The 6800 and 6802 do not have indirect addressing as such but the same result can be obtained by loading the address into the index register and then indexing relative to memory location 0 as shown below:

LDX #n   where n = indirect address
LDAA 0,X   load contents of n to ACC A

Indirect indexed address

The indirect and indexed addressing modes can be combined to provide even more complex addressing modes.

In the indirect indexed mode the effective address is produced by first of all reading the indirect address specified by the instruction operand and then adding the contents of the index register to it. In effect the indirect address gives the start of a table in memory and the index gives the location relative to this start position. For the 6502 this addressing mode would use the following instruction:

LDA (n),Y

Here the address from which data is loaded is obtained by taking the contents of location n and adding the value in Y.

Indexed indirect address

An alternative combination of the indirect and indexed modes is indexed indirect. Here the value in the index register is added to the instruction operand to produce an address in memory from which the effective address is to be read. For the 6502 this instruction would be written as:

LDA (n,X)

Here the effective address from which data is loaded is obtained by adding n to the value in the X register.

Interrupt operations

One important feature which is included on all of the commonly used microprocessors is that of the interrupt operation. This feature allows the CPU to respond directly to external events.

Under normal program operation if the CPU is to respond to, say, the pressing of a key on the keyboard a repeated test of the keyboard status must be built into the program instruction sequence so that when a key is pressed the program can detect this and take appropriate action. In many cases this can be arranged by using a simple polling loop. When a keyboard is required the program goes into a short loop which tests the keyboard status. If no key is pressed the loop repeats the test but when a key press is detected the program goes on to read the keyboard data.

This simple polling process is adequate for situations where the program is waiting for an input but for many applications, particularly where the system has to work in real time, the input condition may occur at any time and the CPU must respond to this situation quickly. The solution is provided by a hardware interrupt input.

The interrupt input is usually labelled INT (interrupt) or IRQ (interrupt request). When an active signal is input to the IRQ line it causes the processor to start an interrupt sequence. Normally the CPU will complete the instruction it is currently executing and then the program counter and status register data are saved. At this point a new address which is the start address for an interrupt service routine is loaded into the PC and the program execution then branches to the interrupt service routine. This routine acts in a similar way to a subroutine and when it is complete the saved program counter and status register values are restored and the main program resumes at the point where it was interrupted.

Since the interrupt routine is triggered by a hardware signal input the CPU can now respond virtually immediately to an external event at any point during the execution of its main program.

Masked and non-masked interrupts

Where the CPU has more than one interrupt input line there is an advantage in being able to disable some of the interrupt inputs so that they cannot interrupt a routine which is time critical. This is achieved by using an interrupt mask system.

Most CPUs have one interrupt input which will always be active. This is generally called a non maskable interrupt (NMI). The other interrupt inputs are usually masked. In a masked interrupt the state of a data bit in the CPU status register will determine whether the CPU will respond to the interrupt. When this bit is set the interrupt input is ignored (or masked) whilst if the bit is at zero the interrupt is processed normally. Some CPUs have two or more masked interrupt inputs and each has its own mask bit in the status register.

Software interrupts

Some processors such as the 6800 and 6809 have an instruction called SWI (software interrupt). When this instruction is executed it generates an interrupt and calls an interrupt service routine. It might seem that this does the same thing as a simple subroutine call but the action is different since the instruction triggers an interrupt. On the 6502 processor the software interrupt instruction is called break (BRK).

Software interrupts are generally used for debugging of software since they can be used to insert breakpoints into the program so that when the breakpoint or SWI instruction is reached the interrupt routine can for instance cause the register contents to be printed out.

The 6800 provides a series of TRAP instructions for its software interrupt facility. These each have their own interrupt vector and can be used to call a range of different routines.

Interrupt vectors

In order to call the interrupt service routine the CPU must obtain the address of the first instruction of the routine and load it into the program counter. This routine start address is usually held in a pair of memory locations which are generally referred to as the interrupt vector. Most CPUs have specific address locations set aside for the vectors of each of their interrupt inputs.

As an example the NMI vector for a 6800 is located at memory addresses FFFC and FFFD whilst the IRQ vector is at addresses FFF8 and FFF9. In the Z80 CPU the vector addresses are usually at the bottom of the memory map.

Some processors expect to obtain the interrupt routine address from the external device that caused the interrupt. In this case an INTA (interrupt acknowledge) signal is sent out after the IRQ input has been received. The CPU then expects to be able to read the address data via the data bus.

Interrupt priority

In a system which has several interrupt inputs some of the inputs must be able to respond quickly whilst others which are servicing slower devices such as printers can wait for a short time. It is therefore useful to have a priority system which allows some interrupts to interrupt a lower priority service routine.

Usually the RESET input will have the highest priority. NMI normally has higher priority than a standard IRQ input. This priority scheme is usually built into the CPU itself. Where there are several inputs feeding the same IRQ input line an external priority encoder can be used to allocate priority levels to the various interrupt inputs.

Interrupt service routines

When an interrupt occurs the program execution branches to a location specified by the interrupt vector and at this point in memory there should be an interrupt service routine which will handle the required response to the interrupt. This routine is similar to a subroutine except that at the end a return from interrupt (RTI) instruction is included which performs a slightly different action from an RTS instruction. Some processors such as the Z80 use the same return instruction for both interrupt handlers and subroutines. On the 6800 the instruction is RTE (return from exception).

In processors such as the 6809 the interrupt causes all of the CPU registers to be saved to the stack before the interrupt service routine starts executing. Most other processors save only the program counter and status registers. In this latter case if any of the CPU registers are to be used in the interrupt routine then their existing contents must be saved at the start of the routine and then restored before the return instruction so that when the main program resumes the CPU registers will be as they were before the interrupt occurred.

When an interrupt is executed it is usual for the CPU to set the interrupt mask so that any further interrupts on that input are not acted upon. If the mask bit is cleared during the service routine this will allow further interrupts to occur and thus the service routine can itself be interrupted.

5 8-bit processors

Rockwell 6502

The 6502 processor originally developed by MOS Technology was based to some extent on the philosophy of the Motorola 6800 but with a simpler architecture and instruction set. This processor became very popular in personal computers and is used in the Apple II, BBC Micro, Atari XE, Commodore PET and others. The Commodore 64 uses the 6510 which is a variant of the 6502. The 65C02 is a CMOS version of the 6502 which has an extended instruction set.

Figure 38 shows the five internal registers of the 6502 which can be accessed by the program. An 8-bit accumulator (A) is used for data manipulation and arithmetic. A processor status register (P) provides the usual flag bits for negative (N), zero (Z), carry (C) and overflow error (V), as shown in Figure 39. The decimal bit (D) is used to indicate that the accumulator is working in BCD mode and the interrupt bit (I) is used to set the interrupt mask. Finally a break bit (B) provides a software interrupt facility.

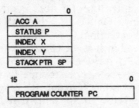

Figure 38 The internal registers of a 6502 CPU

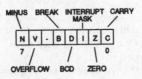

Figure 39 Status register bits of the 6502

In this processor the stack pointer has only 8 bits so the maximum length of the stack is 256 bytes. The stack is always located in page 1 of the memory map starting at location $1FF hex. and extending down to location $100. The 6502 has two 8-bit index registers (X) and (Y). Indexing can only extend for 255 locations beyond the specified memory address. Finally the 16-bit program counter (PC) allows direct access to 64k bytes of memory.

The 6502 uses a 40-pin DIL package with connections as shown in Figure 40.

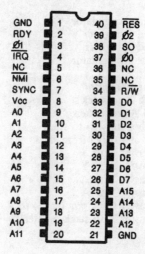

Figure 40   Pin connections of the 6502

Signal functions

A0–A15	16-bit address bus (output)
D0–D7	8-bit data bus (bidirectional)
R/W	Read/write control. Write = 0
IRQ	Interrupt request input (active low)
NMI	Non maskable interrupt input (active low)
RESET	Reset input (active low)
CLK	Clock input
SY	Output indicating instruction fetch cycle
HALT	Halt input

Power supply Vcc = + 4.75 V to + 5.25 V 150 mA

Bus timing

The 6502 has a simple two-phase clock system and each instruction cycle uses one clock cycle. The CPU accesses the data bus when the phase 2 clock signal is high. Decoding of the opcode and other internal activity occurs when the phase 1 clock signal is high.

Instruction set

Data transfer

LDA	Load accumulator
LDX	Load X register
LDY	Load Y register
STA	Store accumulator
STX	Store X register
STY	Store Y register
PHA	Push A to stack
PLA	Pull A from stack
PHP	Push status (P) to stack
PLP	Pull status (P) from stack
TAX	Transfer A to X
TAY	Transfer A to Y
TXA	Transfer X to A
TYA	Transfer Y to A
TSX	Transfer stack pointer (S) to X
TXS	Transfer X to stack pointer (S)

Arithmetic

ADC	Add with carry
SBC	Subtract with carry
INC	Increment memory
DEC	Decrement memory
INX	Increment X register
DEX	Decrement X register
INY	Increment Y register
DEY	Decrement Y register
CMP	Compare with accumulator (A)
CPX	Compare with X register
CPY	Compare with Y register

Logic

AND	Logical AND with accumulator
EOR	Exclusive OR with accumulator
ORA	Inclusive OR with accumulator
LSR	Logic shift right by one bit
ASL	Arithmetic shift left by one bit

ROL	Rotate left by one bit
ROR	Rotate right by one bit
CLC	Clear carry bit
CLD	Clear decimal flag
CLI	Clear interrupt mask bit
CLV	Clear overflow V bit
SEC	Set carry bit
SED	Set decimal flag
SEI	Set interrupt mask bit
SEV	Set overflow V bit
BIT	Bitwise compare with A

Branch and jump

BCC	Branch if carry clear (C = 0)
BCS	Branch if carry set (C = 1)
BEQ	Branch if zero (Z = 1)
BMI	Branch if minus (N = 1)
BNE	Branch if not zero (Z = 0)
BPL	Branch if plus (N = 0)
BVC	Branch if overflow Clear (V = 0)
BVS	Branch if overflow Set (V = 1)
JMP	Jump to address
JSR	Jump to subroutine

Miscellaneous

NOP	No operation
BRK	Break (software interrupt)
RTS	Return from subroutine
RTI	Return from interrupt routine

Address modes

Implied	Internal register operations
Immediate	Loads next byte as constant
Page Zero	Accesses $000 to $0FF in memory
Absolute	Uses 2 byte operand address
Relative	1 byte offset (all branches)
Indexed	X or Y plus 1 byte operand
Indirect	Takes address from page zero
Indirect indexed	Uses Y register for index
Indexed indirect	Uses X register for index

Implied addressing is used for operations on or between internal registers such as CLR A, TAX and LSR A. Immediate addressing is used for loading constants to registers.

Absolute addressing uses a 2 byte address operand and can access a 64k byte memory area. Page zero addressing uses a 1 byte address to access locations 0 to 255. Indexed addressing uses contents of either the X or Y register added to the operand byte to give effective address. Index range is from 0 to 255 and is always positive relative to the base address. Page zero indexed addressing may be used with the Y register only for LDX and STX instructions. Branch instructions all use relative addressing with an 8-bit offset.

Indirect addressing uses the operand to point to the lower of a pair of locations in page zero from which the effective address is loaded. Two successive memory bytes are used as the effective address with the MSB in the higher memory location. This mode is only available for JMP instruction. Indirect indexed addressing uses the operand to load an indirect address from page zero and then adds the contents of Y to this address to produce the effective address. Indexed indirect adds the operand to the contents of the X register to give a page zero address from which the effective address is read.

Instruction timing

Mode	Bytes	Cycles
Implied	1	2
Immediate	2	2
Page zero	2	3
Absolute	3	4
Indexed	2	4
Indirect	2	5
Indirect indexed	2	5
Indexed indirect	2	6
Relative	2	2/3

Implied instructions take two clock cycles. The first cycle is used to fetch the instruction opcode and the instruction is executed in the second cycle. Other address modes use extra cycles for loading operands and internal operations. Shift and rotate operations of memory locations take two extra cycles for internal operation.

The execution time for branch instructions is normally two cycles if no branch is made but increases to three or four cycles when a branch is executed. The higher value is when the branch is to a different page of memory.

Interrupts

The 6502 provides a non masked interrupt (NMI) and a masked interrupt (IRQ) which are hardware triggered by a high/low transition on the appropriate input. A software interrupt is provided by the BRK instruction. The interrupt vectors are held in the top 6 bytes of memory.

Address	Vector
$FFFE/F	IRQ and BRK
$FFFC/D	RESET
$FFFA/B	NMI

The IRQ and BRK interrupts share the same vector so the interrupt service routine must first determine whether IRQ or BRK caused the interrupt. In the status (P) register the B bit is set when a BRK instruction is executed. For interrupts only the return address and status register are saved on the stack.

Motorola 6802

The first 8-bit processor from Motorola was the 6800 which needed an external clock generator. The later 6802 has the same basic architecture and instruction set as the 6800 but includes a built in clock generator and a small amount of on chip RAM. The 6808 is a version with no on chip RAM.

The register set of the 6802 is shown in Figure 41. Two 8-bit accumulators ACCA and ACCB may be used independently for arithmetic and logic operations. Unlike the 6502 with its limited indexing range the 6802 has a 16-bit index register X which allows indexed addressing throughout the entire 64k memory range. Similarly, the 16-bit stack pointer (SP) allows stacks to be located anywhere in memory. The condition code register (CCR) shown in Figure 42 provides the usual Z, N, C and V status flags for conditional instructions. There is also a half carry flag H which is used in BCD arithmetic and an interrupt mask flag I. A 16-bit program counter (PC) completes the 6802 register set and allows access to 64k bytes of memory.

The 6802 comes in a 40-pin DIL package with the connections shown in Figure 43.

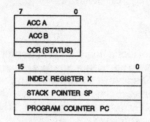

Figure 41 Internal registers of the 6802 CPU

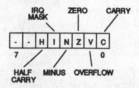

Figure 42 The condition code register (CCR) of the 6802

GND	1	40	RES
HALT	2	39	X2
MR	3	38	X1
IRQ	4	37	E
VMA	5	36	RE
NMI	6	35	VSBY
BA	7	34	R/W
Vcc	8	33	D0
A0	9	32	D1
A1	10	31	D2
A2	11	30	D3
A3	12	29	D4
A4	13	28	D5
A5	14	27	D6
A6	15	26	D7
A7	16	25	A15
A8	17	24	A14
A9	18	23	A13
A10	19	22	A12
A11	20	21	GND

Figure 43 Pin connections for the 6802

Signal functions

A0–A15	Address bus output
D0–D7	Data bus (bidirectional)
X, EX	Timing crystal
R/W	Read/write output (W = 0)
VMA	Valid memory address output
BA	Bus available output
RE	RAM enable input
E	Enable clock output
MR	Memory ready input
VSBY	Standby power input for RAM
NMI	Non-masked interrupt input
IRQ	Interrupt input
RES	Reset input
HALT	Halt input

Power supply Vcc = + 4.75 V to + 5.25 V 130 mA

The HALT, RESET and both interrupt inputs are all
active low.

Instruction set

The instruction set of the 6802 is the same as that of
the earlier 6800 and contains seventy-two instructions.

Data Transfer

LDAA	Load ACC A from memory
LDAB	Load ACC B from memory
LDS	Load stack pointer (SP)
LDX	Load index register
PSHA	Push data from ACC A to stack
PSHB	Push data from ACC B to stack
PULA	Pull data from stack to ACC A
PULB	Pull data from stack to ACC B
STAA	Store ACC A to memory
STAB	Store ACC B to memory
STS	Store SP to memory
STX	Store X register to memory
TAB	Copy ACC A to ACC B
TAP	Copy A or B to CCR (status)
TBA	Copy ACC B to ACC A
TPA	Copy CCR to A or B
TSX	Copy SP to X register
TXS	Copy X register to SP

Arithmetic

ADDA	Add to ACC A
ADDB	Add to ACC B
ADCA	Add with carry to ACC A
ADCB	Add with carry to ACC B
ABA	Add B to A
DAA	Decimal adjust accumulator
DEC	Decrement memory
DECA	Decrement ACC A
DECB	Decrement ACC B
DES	Decrement SP
DEX	Decrement X register
INC	Increment memory
INCA	Increment ACC A
INCB	Increment ACC B
INS	Increment SP
INX	Increment X register
NEG	Negate memory
NEGA	Negate ACC A
NEGB	Negate ACC B
SBA	Subtract B from A
SBCA	Subtract with carry from ACC A
SBCB	Subtract with carry from ACC B
SUBA	Subtract from ACC A
BITA	Bit test on ACC A
BITB	Bit test on ACC B
CMPA	Compare ACC A with memory
CMPB	Compare ACC B with memory
CBA	Compare A with B
TST	Test memory word
TSTA	Test ACC A
TSTB	Test ACC B

Logical

ANDA	AND ACC A with data
ANDB	AND ACC B with data
ORA	OR ACC A with data
ORB	OR ACC B with data
EORA	Exclusive OR ACC A with data
EORB	Exclusive OR ACC B with data
COM	Complement memory word
COMA	Complement ACC A
COMB	Complement ACC B
CLR	Set memory word to zero
CLRA	Clear ACC A

CLRB	Clear ACC B
ASL	Arithmetic shift left memory
ASLA	Arithmetic shift left ACC A
ASLB	Arithmetic shift left ACC B
ASR	Arithmetic shift right memory
ASRA	Arithmetic shift right ACC A
ASRB	Arithmetic shift right ACC B
LSR	Logic shift right memory
LSRA	Logic shift right ACC A
LSRB	Logic shift right ACC B
ROL	Rotate left via carry memory
ROLA	Rotate left via carry ACC A
ROLB	Rotate left via carry ACC B
ROR	Rotate right via carry memory
RORA	Rotate right via carry ACC A
RORB	Rotate right via carry ACC B
CLC	Clear carry flag
CLI	Clear interrupt mask flag
CLV	Clear overflow (V) flag
SEC	Set carry flag
SEI	Set interrupt mask flag
SEV	Set overflow (V) flag

Branch and jump

BCC	Branch if carry clear
BCS	Branch if carry set
BEQ	Branch if zero
BNE	Branch if not zero
BGE	Branch if greater or zero
BGT	Branch if greater than
BHI	Branch if higher
BLE	Branch if less or equal
BLS	Branch if lower or same
BPL	Branch if plus ($N = 0$)
BMI	Branch if minus ($N = 1$)
BVC	Branch if overflow clear ($V = 0$)
BVS	Branch if overflow set ($V = 1$)
BRA	Branch always
JMP	Jump to address
BSR	Branch to subroutine
JSR	Jump to subroutine

Miscellaneous

| NOP | No operation |
| RTI | Return from interrupt |

RTS	Return from subroutine
SWI	Software interrupt
WAI	Wait for interrupt

Address Modes

Implied	For internal register operation
Immediate	Loads operand to register
Page zero	Accesses locations $000–$0FF
Absolute	2-byte operand gives address
Relative	1-byte operand as offset
Indexed	1-byte operand + index = address

The 6802 uses implied register addressing to access and transfer data between the internal registers. Accumulators A or B are selected by adding A or B to the mnemonic (i.e., LDAA, EORB etc.). Immediate addressing is used for loading constants into registers. Memory addressing modes are direct (page zero), absolute and indexed. In the indexed mode an 8-bit base address read from memory is added to the index register contents to give the effective address. All branches use relative addressing with an 8-bit offset. Unlike the 6502 this processor does not have an indirect addressing mode but similar results can be achieved by loading the memory data to the index register and then using indexed addressing with a base address of zero.

Instruction timing and memory usage for the various address modes are:

Mode	Bytes	Cycles
Implied	1	2
Immediate	2	2
Page zero	2	3
Absolute	3	4
Indexed	2	5
Relative	2	4

Instructions such as BSR, JSR, interrupts and returns take longer to execute because they involve moving data to or from the stack. In interrupts all internal registers are automatically saved to the stack.

If the internal RAM is enabled by the RE input it will occupy the addresses $0000 to $007F. The first 32 bytes of this RAM may be maintained during power down periods by a standby supply.

The interrupt vectors for the 6802 are located at the top of the memory as follows:

$FFFE/F	Restart triggered by RES
$FFFC/D	Non-masked interrupt (NMI)
$FFFA/B	Software interrupt (SWI)
$FFF8/9	Maskable interrupt (IRQ)

Each vector is a 16-bit word occupying two memory bytes with the MSB in the lower memory address. Interrupt priority has RES as the highest and works down in order to IRQ as the lowest.

Motorola 6809

The 6809 is an enhanced version of the 6800 with more internal registers and some additional instructions. The 6809E is a variant of the 6809 without the built in clock circuit. Faster versions are available with type numbers 68A09 and 68B09.

The register set of the 6809 is shown in Figure 44. The two accumulator registers ACCA and ACCB may be used together to provide double length accumulator (ACCD) for 16-bit arithmetic operations. Two 16-bit index registers X and Y permit indexed addressing through the entire 64k memory address space. Two 16-bit stack pointers USP and SSP are provided. Pointer SSP is automatically used by interrupts and subroutine calls for saving register data. A condition code register CCR provides status flag bits shown in Figure 45 and there is a 16-bit program counter (PC).

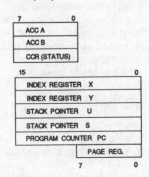

Figure 44 Internal register set of the 6809 CPU

Figure 45 The 6809 condition code register (CCR)

The 6809 comes in a 40-pin DIL package with pin connections as shown in Figure 46.

Figure 46 Pin connections for the 6809

6809 Signals

D0–D7	Data bus (bidirectional)
A0–A15	Address bus (output)
R/W	Read/write control output
IRQ	Maskable interrupt input (active low)
FIRQ	Maskable interrupt input (active low)
NMI	Non-maskable interrupt input
BREQ	Bus request input
MR	Memory ready input
BA	Bus available output
BS	Bus status output
HALT	Halt input
Q	Quadrature clock output
E	Enable (phase 2) clock output

Power supply Vcc = +4.75 V to +5.25 V 200 mA

The quadrature clock output is a quarter of a cycle out of phase relative to the E clock.

Instruction set

The instruction set is upward compatible with that of the 6800 or 6802 CPU but some instruction mnemonics are different.

Data transfer

LDAA, LDAB	Load accumulator A or B
STAA, STAB	Store accumulator A or B
LDS, LDU	Load stack pointer S or U
LDX, LDY	Load index register X or Y
STS, STU	Store stack pointer
STX, STY	Store index register
LEAS, LEAU	Effective address to stack pointer
LEAX, LEAY	Effective address to index register
PSHS, PSHU	Push S or U to stack
PULS, PULU	Pull S or U from stack
TFR r1,r2	Transfer 16-bit from r1 to r2
EXG r1,r2	Exchange 16-bit registers r1 and r2
LDD	Load 16-bits to ACCD
STD	Store 16-bits from ACCD

R1, R2 are 16-bit registers ACCD, X, Y, SSP, USP and PC

Arithmetic

ADDA, ADDB	Add to accumulator A or B
ADCA, ADCB	Add with carry to A or B
SUBA, SUBB	Subtract from accumulator A or B
SBCA, SBCB	Subtract with carry from A or B
ADDD	Add to ACCD (16-bit)
SUBD	Subtract from ACCD (16-bit)
MUL	Multiply A by B (result in ACCD)
NEGA, NEGB	Negate A or B
INCA, INCB	Increment A or B
DECA, DECB	Decrement A or B
DAA	Decimal adjust A accumulator
CMPA, CMPB	Compare with accumulator
CMPD	Compare ACCD with memory

CMPS, CMPU	Compare SP with memory
CMPX, CMPY	Compare index register with memory
SEX	Sign extend ACCD

Logical

ANDA, ANDB	AND with A or B
ANDD	AND with ACCD (16-bit)
ANDCC	AND with CCR
ORA. ORB	OR with A or B
ORCC	OR with CCR
EORA, EORB	EXCLUSIVE OR with A or B
LSLA, LSLB	Left shift A or B
LSL	Left shift memory
ASLA, ASLB	Arithmetic shift left ACCA or ACCB
ASL	Arithmetic shift left memory
LSRA, LSRB	Shift right ACCA or ACCB
LSR	Shift right memory
ROLA, ROLB	Rotate left ACCA or ACCB
RORA, RORB	Rotate right via carry ACCA or ACCB

Branch and jump

BCC, LBCC	Branch if carry clear
BCS, LBCS	Branch if carry set
BEQ, LBEQ	Branch if equal
BNE, LBNE	Branch if not equal
BPL, LBPL	Branch if plus
BMI, LBMI	Branch if minus
BVC, LBVC	Branch if overflow clear
BVS, LBVS	Branch if overflow set
BRA, LBRA	Branch always
BRN, LBRN	Branch never
BGE, LBGE	Branch if greater or equal
BGT, LBGT	Branch if greater than
BLE, LBLE	Branch if less or equal
BLT, LBLT	Branch if less than
BHI, LBHI	Branch if higher (unsigned)
BHS, LBHS	Branch if higher or same (unsigned)
BLO, LBLO	Branch if lower (unsigned)
BLS, LBLS	Branch if lower or same

	(unsigned)
BSR, LBSR	Branch to subroutine
JMP	Jump to address
JSR	Jump to subroutine

Long branch instructions such as LBEQ have a 16-bit offset.

Miscellaneous

NOP	No operation
RTI	Return from interrupt
RTS	Return from subroutine
SWI	Software interrupt 1
SWI2	Software interrupt 2
SWI3	Software interrupt 3
SYNC	Synchronize with interrupt
CWAI	AND CCR then wait for interrupt

Interrupts

The 6809 provides three software interrupts (SWI, SWI2 and SWI3) where SWI has the highest priority and SWI3 the lowest. Hardware interrupts are reset (RES), non masked interrupt (NMI) and two masked interrupts IRQ and FIRQ. The IRQ interrupt causes all registers to be saved to the stack whilst FIRQ causes only the return address and status to be saved on the stack. RTI automatically restores the appropriate registers. The 6809 uses fixed interrupt vector locations at the top of memory.

Address	Interrupt vector
$FFFF/$FFFE	RESET
$FFFD/$FFFC	NMI
$FFFB/$FFFA	SWI
$FFF9/$FFF8	IRQ
$FFF7/$FFF6	FIRQ
$FFF5/$FFF4	SWI2
$FFF3/$FFF2	SWI3

Interrupt priority has reset as highest and SWI3 as lowest in the order the vectors are stored in memory.

The 6809 has the same basic clock and instruction timing as the 6802 with each instruction cycle taking up one clock period. Memory access occurs during phase 2 of the clock when the E signal output is high.

Intel 8085A

The 8085A is a development of the earlier Intel 8080 processor. Whereas the earlier processor required an external clock generator and some external chips to control its bus system the 8085 has these features built into the chip. Other enhancements included in the 8085A are a serial input–output facility and some additional interrupt facilities. The basic instruction set is upward compatible with that of the 8080 so that programs written for the 8080 will run on the 8085A.

The 8085A has 16-bit program counter (PC) and stack pointer (SP) registers allowing access to 64k bytes of memory and flexible stack operation. An 8-bit Accumulator A and six 8-bit working registers B, C, D, E, H and L are provided as shown in Figure 47. There is also a flag (status) register F with bits allocated as shown in Figure 48.

15 ... 8	7 ... 0	
ACC A	FLAGS F	PSW
REG B	REG C	BC
REG D	REG E	DE
REG H	REG L	HL

15 ... 0
STACK POINTER SP (16 BIT)
PROGRAM COUNTER PC (16 BIT)

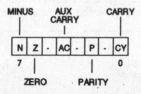

Figure 47 The internal registers of the 8085A CPU

Figure 48 The flag register of the 8085A

Register pairs BC, DE and HL may be used as 16-bit registers and for indirect addressing. The HL register pair may be also be used as a 16-bit index register and for some 16-bit arithmetic operations.

The 8085A has an 8-bit data bus and a 16-bit address bus which permits up to 64k bytes of memory to be addressed directly. Input and output channels can be addressed separately from memory using the

lower byte of the address bus in conjunction with the
M/I–O control line and allows up to 256 input–
output channels to be addressed directly.

The signals for the data bus share the same set of
pins on the chip as the lower byte of the address bus
and a control line address latch enable (ALE) is used
to indicate when an address is being output on these
pins. Because the address and data lines are
multiplexed in this way an external 8-bit latch is
required to hold the lower byte of the address whilst
the actual data transfer is made.

The 8085A has a 40-pin DIL package with connections as shown in Figure 49.

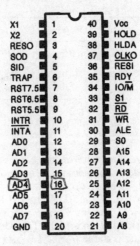

Figure 49 Pin connections for the 8085A

8085A signals

AD0–AD7	Multiplexed address/data bus
A8–A15	Address bus
ALE	Address latch enable
RD	Read control output
WR	Write control output
IO/M	I–O/memory select output
RST	Restart interrupt inputs
INTR	Interrupt input
INTA	Interrupt acknowledge output
HOLD	Hold input
HLDA	Hold acknowledge output

X1,X2	Clock crystal
CLKO	Clock output
S0, S1	Bus status outputs
TRAP	Trap interrupt input
SID	Serial data input
SOD	Serial data output
RESI	Reset input
RESO	Reset output
RDY	Ready input

Power supply $Vcc = +4.75$ V to $+5.25$ V 170 mA

Bus status coding

S1	S0	Bus state
0	0	Halt
0	1	Write cycle
1	0	Read cycle
1	1	Opcode fetch

Bus timing

Instruction cycles consist of three or more clock periods. Opcode fetch cycles have four clock periods (T1 to T4) whilst other cycles normally have three periods (T1 to T3). If the RDY input is low during T2 then extra wait periods Tw are inserted between T2 and T3 until RDY goes high. The address is set up during T1 and is stable when ALE goes to 0. Data may be set up during T2 and is transferred during T3.

The HOLD input acts as a bus request and the CPU will release the buses at the end of the current instruction cycle. HLDA output goes high to indicate that the buses have been released.

Instruction set

Data transfer

MOV r1 r2	Move from r2 to r1
MOV M.r	Move from r indirect to (HL)
MOV r.M	Move indirect from (HL) to r
MVI r	Move immediate to r
MVI M	Move immediate to memory
LXI rr	Load immediate register pair

	BC, DE or HL
LHLD	Load HL from memory
SHLD	Store HL to memory
XCHG	Exchange D with E and H with L
STAX	Store A indirect to (BC) or (DE)
LDAX	Load A indirect from (BC) or (DE)
LDA addr	Load A from memory at address
STA addr	Store A to memory at address
PUSH	Push to stack (BC,DE,HL or AF)
POP	Pop from stack (BC,DE,HL or AF)
SPHL	Move HL to SP
XTHL	Move SP to HL
LXI SP	Load immediate data to SP
INX SP	Increment SP
DCX SP	Decrement SP
RIM	Read interrupt mask
SIM	Set interrupt mask
IN port	Input from port to A
OUT port	Output to port from A

Arithmetic

ADD r	Add register $A = A + r$
ADD M	Add indirect $A = A + (HL)$
ADI data	Add immediate $A = A + data$
ADC r	Add with carry $A = A + r + CY$
ADC M	Add with carry $A = A + (HL) + CY$
ACI data	Add with carry $A = A + data + CY$
SUB r	Subtract register $A = A - r$
SUB M	Subtract indirect $A = A - (HL)$
SUI data	Subtract immediate $A = A - data$
SBB r	Subtract with borrow $A = A - r - CY$
SBB M	Subtract with borrow $A = A - (HL) - CY$
SBI data	Subtract with borrow $A = A - data - CY$
DAD rr	Double add $HL = HL + rr$
	(rr = register pair BC, DE or HL)
DAA	Decimal adjust A (for BCD arithmetic)
INR r	Increment register r
INR M	Increment indirect memory at (HL)
INX rr	Increment register pair rr
DCR r	Decrement register r
DCR M	Decrement indirect memory at (HL)
DCX rr	Decrement register pair rr
CMP r	Compare A with register r
CMP M	Compare A indirect with memory
CPI data	Compare A immediate with data

Logical

ANA r	AND A with register r
ANA M	AND A indirect with memory at (HL)
ANI data	AND A immediate with data
XRA r	EXCLUSIVE OR A with register r
XRA M	EXCLUSIVE OR A indirect with memory at (HL)
XRI data	EXCLUSIVE OR A immediate with data
ORA r	OR A with register r
ORA M	OR A indirect with memory at (HL)
ORI data	OR A immediate with data
RLC	Rotate A left
RRC	Rotate A right
RAL	Rotate A left through CY
RAR	Rotate A right through CY
CMA	Complement A
CMC	Complement carry CY flag bit
STC	Set CY flag bit

Branch and jump

JMP	Unconditional jump
Jcc	Conditional jump if cc is true
PCHL	Indirect jump to address in HL
CALL	Call subroutine
Ccc	Call subroutine if condition cc is true

Condition codes cc are as follows:

NZ	Not zero	Z bit = 0
Z	Zero	Z bit = 1
NC	No carry	CY bit = 0
C	Carry	CY bit = 1
PO	Parity odd	P bit = 0
PE	Parity even	P bit = 1
P	Plus	S bit = 0
M	Minus	S bit = 1

For example instruction JNZ causes a jump if $Z = 1$ otherwise program continues in normal sequence.

Miscellaneous

EI	Enable interrupts
DI	Disable interrupts

HLT	Halt the CPU
NOP	No operation
RET	Return from subroutine or interrupt
Rcc	Conditional return if cc is true
RST n	Restart (software interrupt)

Instruction timing

First instruction cycle is opcode fetch which takes four clock periods and other instruction cycles normally use three clock periods. Wait states may be added if slow memory or peripherals are being accessed.

Mode	Bytes	Cycles
Register (implied)	1	1
Immediate 8 bit	2	2
Immediate 16 bit	3	3
Absolute	3	4
Register indirect	1	2

Conditional instruction cycle times vary according to the type of operation and whether the condition is true or false.

Interrupts

The TRAP input is effectively a non-masked hardware interrupt. The restart instructions RST n where n = 0 to 7 are software interrupts. Three further restart interrupts RST5.5, RST6.5 and RST7.5 are hardware triggered from the RST inputs. These interrupts all use direct vectoring.

Interrupt	Vector address
TRAP	$24
RST 0	$00
RST 1	$08
RST 2	$10
RST 3	$18
RST 4	$20
TRAP	$24
RST 5	$28
RST 5.5	$2C

RST 6	$30
RST 6.5	$34
RST 7	$38
RST 7.5	$3C

A hardware RESET input sets the program counter at zero and produces a similar effect to RST 0.

An INT input starts an interrupt cycle and is acknowledged by an output on the INTA line. At this point the CPU expects to read either a CALL or RST opcode on the data bus and this must be supplied by the interrupting hardware device.

Zilog Z80

The Z80, developed by Zilog, is based on the Intel 8080 but has a much larger instruction set and uses a different bus structure. The National NSC800 is a CMOS equivalent for the Z80.

The Z80 has two 16-bit index registers IX and IY, a 16-bit stack pointer and 16-bit program counter as shown in Figure 50. There are two banks of working registers. Register A is an 8-bit accumulator. Registers B, C, D, E, H and L are 8-bit registers which may also be used as 16-bit register pairs BC, DE and HL. This register bank is the same as that in the Intel 8085. The flag register bits are allocated as shown in Figure 51. This entire bank of registers is duplicated and the alternate set of these registers can be selected by a software instruction. Two further 8-bit registers are the I and R registers. The I register provides the high byte of the interrupt vector address in one mode of interrupt operation. The R register can be used to provide an address output for refreshing dynamic memories.

The Z80 uses a 40-pin DIL package with pin connections as shown in Figure 52.

Signal lines

A0–A15	Address bus (output)
D0–D7	Data bus (bidirectional)
M1	Opcode fetch status output
MREQ	Memory request output
IORQ	Input–output request output
RD	Read control output
WR	Write control output
NMI	Non-maskable interrupt input

MAIN REGISTERS (8 BIT)		
ACC A	FLAG F	PSW
REG B	REG C	BC
REG D	REG E	DE
REG H	REG L	HL

ALTERNATE REGISTERS (8 BIT)		
ACC A'	FLAG F'	PSW'
REG B'	REG C'	BC'
REG D'	REG E'	DE'
REG H'	REG L'	HL'

SYSTEM REGISTERS
INT. VECTOR IV   REFRESH R
INDEX REGISTER IX (16 BIT)
INDEX REGISTER IY (16 BIT)
STACK POINTER SP (16 BIT)
PROGRAM COUNTER PC (16 BIT)

Figure 50 Internal registers of the Z80 CPU

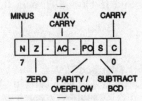

Figure 51 The Z80 flag register

Figure 52 Pin connections for the Z80

IRQ	Maskable interrupt request input
WAIT	Wait input
BUSRQ	Bus request input
BUSAK	Bus acknowledge output
HALT	Halt status output
RFSH	Refresh status output
CLK	Clock input
RES	Reset input

Power supply Vcc = +4.75 V to +5.25 V 200 mA

Instruction set

Data transfer

LD SP	Load stack pointer from HL, IX or IY
PUSH	Push 16-bit register data to stack
POP	Pull 16-bit register data from stack

Arithmetic

ADD	8-bit add to A
ADC	8-bit add with carry to A
SUB	8-bit subtract from A
SBC	8-bit subtract with carry from A
ADD HL	16-bit add to HL register pair
ADC HL	16-bit add with carry to HL
SBC HL	16-bit subtract with carry from HL
ADD IX	16-bit add to register IX
ADD IY	16-bit add to register IY
NEG	Negate contents of A
DAA	Convert result to BCD

Logic operations

AND	AND with A
OR	Inclusive OR with A
XOR	Exclusive OR with A

Branch and Jump

JP	Unconditional jump
JR	Unconditional branch (relative addr.)
JP cc	Conditional jump
JR cc	Conditional branch (relative addr.)

JP (ss)	Indirect jump
DJNZ	Dec B and branch if B = 0
CALL	Jump to subroutine
CALL cc	Conditional jump to subroutine

Miscellaneous

NOP	No operation
HALT	Halt processor
DI	Disable interrupts
EI	Enable interrupts
IM n	Set interrupt mode (n = 0, 1 or 2)
RET	Return from subroutine
RET cc	Conditional return from subroutine
RETI	Return from interrupt routine
RETN	Return from NMI routine

Bus timing

An instruction execution cycle is made up from a number of machine cycles each of which normally consists of three clock periods (T1, T2 and T3). During T1 the address is set up on the bus, then during T2 the RD and WR signals are set up and during T3 data transfers are made. The first machine cycle of every instruction is an opcode fetch. This cycle is called M1 and contains an extra clock period T4 during which the opcode that has been fetched is decoded.

If a WAIT input is present during the T2 period of a cycle the CPU inserts wait cycles where no activity occurs. When the WAIT input is removed the CPU goes on to complete the current machine cycle with its T3 period.

Interrupts

The restart software interrupts have the same action and vector addresses as those in the Intel 8085. The NMI interrupt of the Z80 has its interrupt vector at location $66.

The maskable INT interrupt has three modes of operation which may be selected by the IM instruction. In mode 0 this interrupt operates in a similar way to that of the 8085. The Z80 does not, however, have an INTA output but uses IORQ and M1 to indicate interrupt acknowledge. When the INT input is triggered the CPU activates both IORQ and M1 simultaneously and this must be detected externally. When this condition occurs the external device should place the opcode for a Restart (RST) instruction on data bus. The CPU then vectors to the corresponding restart vector.

In mode 1 an INT interrupt uses the vector address for RST 7 at location $38.

In mode 2 the interrupt acknowledge is generated in the same way as for mode 0 but now the external device should place an 8-bit address on the data bus and the contents of the IV register are used as the MSB to form a 16-bit address. This address is the location of the interrupt vector in memory. In this mode the interrupt vector may be placed anywhere in the 64k memory map.

6 16/32-bit processors

Intel 8086 and 8088

The 8086 CPU from Intel, and its 8-bit bus equivalent the 8088, have become popular in small business computers because of their use in the IBM PC and the various clones of this type of computer. The NEC V30 processor is a direct equivalent of the 8086 but with a faster execution speed. The NEC V20 can be used to replace the 8088 CPU. There is also an 8087 arithmetic coprocessor chip which can be used in conjunction with the 8086 or 8088 to speed up floating point arithmetic calculations.

The 8086 has a 16-bit processor with a 20-bit address bus giving access to 1M of memory. The address and data bus pins on this processor are multiplexed in order to reduce the number of pins on the package to 48 as shown in Figure 53. Thus, data bits D0 to D15 share the same pins as address bits A0 to A15. The 8088 is a version of the 8086 tailored to fit into a smaller package by using an 8-bit data bus as shown in Figure 54. The disadvantage of the 8088 is that it is slower than the 8086 because it has to make two data transfer cycles in order to move a 16-bit word across its data bus.

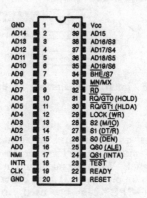

Figure 53 Pin connections for the 8086

```
GND      1      40   Vcc
A14      2      39   A15
A13      3      38   A16/S3
A12      4      37   A17/S4
A11      5      36   A18/S5
A10      6      35   A19/S6
A9       7      34   SSO
A8       8      33   MN/MX
AD7      9      32   RD
AD6     10      31   RQ/GT0 (HOLD)
AD5     11      30   RQ/GT1 (HLDA)
AD4     12      29   LOCK (WR)
AD3     13      28   S2 (M/IO)
AD2     14      27   S1 (DT/R)
AD1     15      26   S0 (DEN)
AD0     16      25   QS0 (ALE)
NMI     17      24   QS1 (INTA)
INTR    18      23   TEST
CLK     19      22   READY
GND     20      21   RESET
```

Figure 54 Pin connections for the 8088

The 8086/88 CPU has a bank of four general-purpose 16-bit registers as shown in Figure 55. Four more registers are used to provide a stack pointer (SP), base address pointer (BP), and two index registers SI and DI. Four segment address registers (CS, DS, SS and ES) are also included together with a program counter PC and status register PSW.

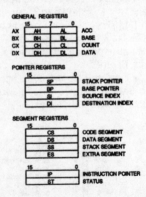

Figure 55 Internal register set of the 8086/8088 CPU

The 8086 and 8088 have two modes of operation known as minimum and maximum mode. In minimum mode the CPU generates its own bus control signals. When the maximum mode is selected the signals on pins 24 to 31 have different functions and the CPU can be used to implement multiprocessor systems.

Signal lines

AD0–AD15	Multiplexed address and data bus
A16/S3–A19/S6	Multiplexed address/status lines
RD	Read control
RESET	Reset input
RDY	Ready input from memory
MN/MX	Minimum/maximum mode select
TEST	Test input
CLK	CPU clock input
INTR	Interrupt input
NMI	Non-masked interrupt input
BHE/S7	High byte enable/status S7 output

Power supply Vcc = +4.75 V to +5.25 V 370 mA

Minimum mode signals (MN/MX=1)

M/I–O	Memory/input-output select output
WR	Write control output
INTA	Interrupt acknowledge output
ALE	Address latch enable output
DT/R	Data transmit/receive output
DEN	Data bus enable output
HOLD	Hold input
HLDA	Hold acknowledge output

Maximum mode signals (MN/MX=0)

RQ/GT0, RQ/GT1	Bus request/grant signals
LOCK	Bus lock (blocks bus requests)
QS0, QS1	Queue status signals
S0, S1, S2	Processor status signals

Processor status codes

Status lines S0–2 indicate the type of cycle being executed and are used by an 8288 bus controller to generate the bus signals for memory and I/O. The action of these lines is shown in Figure 56.

S2	S1	S0	Type of cycle
0	0	0	Interrupt acknowledge
0	0	1	Input from I/O port

0	1	0	Output to I/O port
0	1	1	Halt
1	0	0	Opcode read
1	0	1	Memory read
1	1	0	Memory write
1	1	1	Passive state

S2	S1	S0	TYPE OF CYCLE
0	0	0	INTERRUPT ACKNOWLEDGE
0	0	1	INPUT FROM I/O PORT
0	1	0	OUTPUT TO I/O PORT
0	1	1	HALT
1	0	0	OPCODE READ
1	0	1	MEMORY READ
1	1	0	MEMORY WRITE
1	1	1	PASSIVE STATE

Figure 56 Function of the S0–S2 status lines of the 8086

Bus timing

The normal bus cycle consists of four CPU clock cycles which are labelled T1 to T4. If the RDY input goes low during the T2 clock period then extra Wait cycles are inserted between T3 and T4 to allow slow memories to operate.

During the T1 period the address is output on the address bus. Also during T1 the address latch enable line is pulsed high and the address must be latched externally on the falling edge of the ALE signal.

During T2 the address output is disabled and the data bus is connected to the multiplexed pins. During this period the DEN line is set low to activate the external data bus transceivers.

During T3 data is set up on the data bus and actual data transfer takes place during the T4 period.

Instruction set

Data transfer

MOV	Move byte or word
LEA	Load effective address
LDS	Load pointer using DS
LES	Load pointer using ES
LAHF	Load AH register with flags
SAHF	Store AH register to flags
IN	Input byte or word from port

OUT	Output byte or word to port
PUSH	Push word to stack
POP	Pop word from stack
PUSHA	Push all registers to stack
POPA	Pop all registers from stack
PUSHF	Push flags to stack
POPF	Pop flags from stack
XCHG	Exchange byte or word
XLAT	Translate byte

Arithmetic

ADD	Add word or byte
ADC	Add with carry word or byte
AAA	ASCII adjust for add
DAA	Decimal adjust for BCD add
SUB	Subtract word or byte
SBB	Subtract with borrow word or byte
AAS	ASCII adjust for subtract
DAS	Decimal adjust for BCD subtract
INC	Increment register or memory
DEC	Decrement register or memory
NEG	Negate byte or word
MUL	Unsigned multiply
IMUL	Signed integer multiply
AAM	ASCII adjust for multiply
DIV	Unsigned divide
IDIV	Signed integer divide
AAD	ASCII adjust for divide
CBW	Convert byte to word
CWD	Convert word to double word (32 bits)

Logic

AND	Logical AND
OR	Logical OR
XOR	Exclusive OR
NOT	Invert byte or word
SHL	Shift left one bit
SHR	Shift right one bit
SAR	Arithmetic shift right
ROL	Rotate left
ROR	Rotate right
RCL	Rotate left through carry
RCR	Rotate right through carry
CLC	Clear carry flag

CMC	Complement carry flag
STC	Set carry flag
CLD	Clear direction flag
STD	Set direction flag
CLI	Clear interrupt enable flag
STI	Set interrupt enable flag
TST	Test data and set flags

Branch and jump

CALL	Call subroutine
JMP	Unconditional jump
LOOP	Loop n times (n = contents of CX)
LOOPZ/LOOPE	Loop while zero or equal
LOOPNZ/LOOPNE	Loop while not zero or not equal
JCXZ	Jump when CX = 0
JNS	Jump on not sign
JNO	Jump on not overflow
JZ/JE	Jump on zero (equal)
JO	Jump on overflow
JS	Jump on sign
JL/JNGE	Jump on less (not greater or equal)
JLE/JNG	Jump on less or equal (not greater)
JNL/JGE	Jump on not less (greater or equal)
JB/JNAE	Jump on below (not above or equal)
JPO/JNP	Jump on parity (no parity)
JG/JNLE	Jump on greater than (not less or equal)
JNZ/JNE	Jump on not zero (not equal)
JPE/JP	Jump if parity even or parity
JNA/JBE	Jump if no above (below or equal)
JA/JNBE	Jump if above (not below or equal)

Miscellaneous

HLT	Halt processor
WAIT	Wait
ESC	Escape to external processor
LOCK	Lock bus during next instruction
INT	Interrupt
INTO	Interrupt on overflow
IRET	Return from interrupt routine
RET	Return from subroutine

Instruction timing

The execution of an instruction takes up two or more bus cycles according to the type of operation being carried out. The first cycle is always an opcode fetch which reads in the opcode from memory. If the instruction has an operand then one or more cycles will be used to read the operand and finally one cycle is used to execute the instruction.

Interrupts

The processor supports up to 256 interrupts which may be generated either by hardware or software. Interrupt vectors are located in the memory area $000 to $3FF with 4 bytes for each interrupt vector. For hardware interrupts using the INT input the CPU will output an acknowledge signal on the INTA line at which point the interrupting device should place an interrupt type number from 0 to 255 on the data bus. The appropriate interrupt vector is then located in memory at an address $= 4 \times n$ where n is the interrupt type number. The NMI input generates a type 2 non-maskable interrupt where the vector address is $008. Software interrupts are generated by the INT instruction whose operand is the desired interrupt type number n. A separate software interrupt instruction can directly generate type 3 interrupts without using an operand.

Intel 80186 and 80188

These are enhanced versions of the 8086/88 processors and are packaged in a 68-pin leadless chip carrier.

The instruction set is basically the same as for the

8086/88 type but has the following additional high level instructions:

BOUND   Detects values outside specified range
ENTER   Arrange stack for subroutine entry
LEAVE   Restore stack on subroutine exit

Intel 80286

This is a 16-bit processor with a 16-bit data bus system and is designed to execute programs in 8086 code directly. The major difference in the 286 is that it is designed especially to support the requirements of advanced operating systems and has built in capabilities for multi-tasking where several different programs can be in the process of execution at the same time. Clock speed is higher than for the 8086 and 80186 types to give a higher program execution speed. An arithmetic coprocessor chip type 80287 can be used in conjunction with the 80286 to speed up floating point arithmetic calculations.

Another important feature of the 286 is that it can handle a virtual memory environment. Under these conditions the program is allocated a segment of a virtual memory. Thus a program might be allocated, say, 16k of memory. The processor can now allocate a segment base address for this depending on what parts of the real memory are available. Inside the CPU the virtual address from the program (in the range 0–16k) is translated into a real address in the physical memory each time the program makes a memory reference. By using this type of memory scheme chunks of real memory can be allocated to the various tasks being performed according to the requirements of the various programs.

Intel 80386

This is a full 32-bit processor which has internal 32-bit registers with 32-bit buses for both data and address. There is also an arithmetic coprocessor type 80387 which can be used with the 80386 to speed up floating point arithmetic operations. Like the 286 it supports a virtual memory system and has other advanced features which make it faster in operation than a 286. Software for the 386 is basically upward compatible so that a 386 should be able to run 8086 and 80286 software although the reverse may not be true. Clock speeds up to 25 MHz with the 32-bit architecture make this CPU very much faster than either the 8086 or 80286 types.

Motorola 68000 series

The 68000 processor has proved to be very popular both in personal computers and for dedicated systems because of its power and the versatility of its internal register system which provides full 32-bit operation within the CPU although the data bus is restricted to 16-bit operation. The Hitachi 63000 is a CMOS variant of the 68000. The 68881 is an arithmetic coprocessor which can be used with the 68000 to speed up floating point arithmetic calculations. More advanced processors in this series are the 68010 which provides facilities for virtual memory systems, the 68020 which has the full 32-bit address bus available and the 68030 which provides 32-bit address and data bus systems.

The 68000 contains sixteen registers for handling data and addresses, as shown in Figure 57. All of the registers are 32-bits wide. Registers D0 to D7 are for data handling and all of them may be used as accumulators for arithmetic and logic operations. Registers A0 to A7 provide 32-bit addresses which may be used for indexed operation or indirect addressing. Register A7 is reserved for use as a stack pointer. In fact there are two A7 registers. One is used for the supervisor stack pointer and is used when the processor is in supervisor mode where it is generally carying out system operations. The alternative mode is the user mode when the alternative stack pointer (USP) comes into operation. In the user mode certain parts of the memory and some instructions are not available so that a user cannot easily corrupt the operating system. This is particularly important where several users may have access to the system.

In the 68000 the program counter register provides only twenty-four address bits although the actual register has 32 bits. This provides a memory space of 16M. A status register provides the usual selection of status bits plus further bits for interrupt masking and to show the operating mode of the CPU.

Unlike the 8086, the address and data signals on the 68000 are not multiplexed which makes the bus

31		16	0
	DATA	D0	
	DATA	D1	
	DATA	D2	
	DATA	D3	
	DATA	D4	
	DATA	D5	
	DATA	D6	
	DATA	D7	

	ADDRESS	A0
	ADDRESS	A1
	ADDRESS	A2
	ADDRESS	A3
	ADDRESS	A4
	ADDRESS	A5
	ADDRESS	A6
	ADDRESS	A7 (USP)
	ADDRESS	A7' (SSP)

PROGRAM COUNTER	PC
	STATUS SR

15   0

Figure 57 Internal register set for the 68000 CPU

system a little simpler but does mean that the CPU comes in a 64-lead dual in-line package. The pin connections for the 68000 are shown in Figure 58. A variation of the 68000 is the 68008 processor which is packaged in a 48-lead DIL case, as shown in Figure 59. The 68008 has an 8-bit external data bus although internally the CPU is the same as a 68000.

D4	1	64	D5
D3	2	63	D6
D2	3	62	D7
D1	4	61	D8
D0	5	60	D9
AS	6	59	D10
UDS	7	58	D11
LDS	8	57	D12
R/W	9	56	D13
DTACK	10	55	D14
BG	11	54	D15
BGACK	12	53	GND
BR	13	52	A23
Vcc	14	51	A22
CLK	15	50	A21
GND	16	49	Vcc
HALT	17	48	A20
RESET	18	47	A19
VMA	19	46	A18
E	20	45	A17
VPA	21	44	A16
BERR	22	43	A15
IPL2	23	42	A14
IPL1	24	41	A13
IPL0	25	40	A12
FC2	26	39	A11
FC1	27	38	A10
FC0	28	37	A9
A1	29	36	A8
A2	30	35	A7
A3	31	34	A6
A4	32	33	A5

Figure 58 Pin connections for the 68000

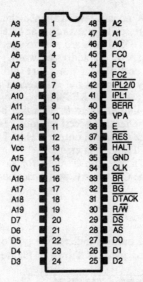

Figure 59 Pin connections for the 68008

Signal functions

A1–A23	23-bit address bus
LDS	Lower data strobe (active low)
UDS	Upper data strobe transfers MS data byte
D0–D15	Data bus lines
R/W	Read/write control output (write = 0)
HALT	Halt input
BERR	Bus error input (active low)
AS	Address Strobe (active low)
CLK	CPU clock
FC0–FC2	Function code outputs
IPL0-IPL2	Interrupt input lines
E	Enable clock output
VMA	Valid memory address out (active low)
VPA	Valid peripheral address in (active low)
BR	Bus request input (active low)
BG	Bus grant output (active low)
BGACK	Bus grant acknowledge in (active low)
DTACK	Data transfer acknowledge out (active low)

Power supply Vcc = +4.75 V to +5.25 V 300 mA

Note there is no address A0 since the processor normally addresses 16-bit words. For byte addressing the LDS and UDS signals are used to select the upper and lower bytes of the addressed word.

The RES and HALT lines are bidirectional. Normally they are inputs but if a RESET instruction is executed it causes the RES line to act as an output and pull the line down to 0. This can be used for resetting peripheral devices without resetting the processor. The CPU will output a HALT signal if it encounters a double bus error.

The DTACK line can be used for slow memory devices and the CPU inserts wait cycles until DTACK goes low.

Bus cycle codes

The FC0–FC2 outputs indicate the type of bus cycle which is taking place as shown in Figure 60.

FC2	FC1	FC0	TYPE OF BUS CYCLE
0	0	0	RESERVED
0	0	1	USER DATA ACCESS
0	1	1	USER PROGRAM ACCESS
0	1	1	RESERVED
1	0	0	RESERVED
1	0	1	SUPERVISOR DATA ACCESS
1	1	0	SUPERVISOR PROGRAM ACCESS
1	1	1	INTERRUPT ACKNOWLEDGE

Figure 60 The FC0–FC2 function codes for the 68000

FC2	FC1	FC0	Type of bus cycle
0	0	0	Reserved
0	0	1	User data access
0	1	0	User program access
0	1	1	Reserved
1	0	0	Reserved
1	0	1	Supervisor data access
1	1	0	Supervisor program access
1	1	1	Interrupt acknowledge

The VPA, VMA and E lines are used when interfacing a 6800 type peripheral device to the 68000 bus. When the peripheral is addressed the VPA line is set low and the CPU starts a special slow bus cycle. The E and VMA signals output by the 68000 correspond to the E and VMA signals used in a 6800 system. The E signal is in fact one tenth that of the 68000 CPU clock.

Bus timing

Each instruction cycle in the 68000 consists of a series of clock states S0–S8 each of which is one half cycle of the CPU clock. For a read cycle there are eight (states S0–S7) and for a write cycle nine states (S0–S8). If a slow memory is being accessed additional wait states will be inserted. Other types of bus cycle such as read-modify-write may use more bus states. Each instruction uses at least one bus cycle for execution and if a memory address has to be generated two or more cycles will be needed. Timing calculation is complex because the 68000 uses a pipeline system in which it may set up a new instruction whilst the current instruction is being executed.

Instruction set

Data transfer

EXG Rx,Ry	Exchange registers Rx and Ry
LEA s,An	Load effective address to An
MOVE s,d	Move data from s to d
MOVEA s,An	Move data to address register An
MOVEM rlst,d	Move multiple registers to memory
MOVEM s,rlst	Move memory to multiple registers
MOVEP Dn,(An)	Move from Dn to a peripheral
MOVEP (An),Dn	Move from peripheral to Dn
MOVEQ #n,Dn	Move immediate data n to Dn
PEA s	Push effective address to stack
SWAP Rn	Swap register halves

Arithmetic

ABCD s,d	Add BCD
ADD s,d	Add binary
ADDA s,d	Add address
ADDI	Add immediate
ADDQ	Add quick
ADDX	Add extended
DIVS	Divide signed numbers
DIVU	Divide unsigned numbers
EXT	Sign extend
MULS	Multiply signed numbers
MULU	Multiply unsigned numbers

NBCD	Negate BCD data
NEG	Negate binary data
NEGX	Negate with extend
SBCD	Subtract BCD numbers
SUB	Subtract binary
SUBA	Subtract address
SUBI	Subtract immediate
SUBQ	Subtract quick
SUBX	Subtract extended
CHK	Test register against limits
CMP	Compare
CMPA	Compare address
CMPI	Compare immediate
CMPM	Compare memory

Logical

AND	Logical AND
ANDI	AND immediate
ASL	Arithmetic shift left
ASR	Arithmetic shift right
CLR	Clear data
EOR	Exclusive OR
EORI	Exclusive OR immediate
LSL	Logic shift left
LSR	Logic shift right
NOT	Logical complement
OR	Logical OR
ORI	OR immediate
RESET	Reset external devices
ROL	Rotate left
ROR	Rotate right
ROXL	Rotate left with extend
ROXR	Rotate right with extend
BSET	Bit test and set bit to 1
BTEST	Bit test
BCHG	Bit test and change state of bit
BCLR	Bit test and clear bit to 0
Scc	Set byte according to cc
TAS	Test byte and set MSB to 1
TST	Test data

Branch and jump

| Bcc | Branch on condition cc |
| BRA | Branch always |

DBcc	Test cc, decrement and branch
JMP ea	Jump to address ea
BSR	Branch to subroutine
JSR ea	Jump to subroutine at ea

Miscellaneous

ILLEGAL	Illegal code
LINK	Link and allocate
NOP	No operation
RTE	Return from exception
RTR	Return and restore cc status
RTS	Return from subroutine
STOP	Load status register and stop
TRAP	Trap (software interrupt)
TRAPV	Trap on overflow
UNLK	Unlink

Condition codes

For some instructions the operation is executed when condition cc is true. The conditions supported by the 68000 are:

cc	Condition	Status bits
EQ	Equal	$Z = 1$
NE	Not equal	$Z = 0$
PL	Plus	$N = 0$
MI	Minus	$N = 1$
CC	Carry Clear	$C = 0$
CS	Carry Set	$C = 1$
VC	Overflow (V) Clear	$V = 0$
VS	Overflow (V) Set	$V = 1$
HI	High	$C = 0, Z = 0$
LS	Low or Same	$C = 1$ or $Z = 1$
HS	High or Same	$C = 0$
LO	Low	$C = 1$
GE	Greater or Equal	$N = 1, V = 1$ or $N = 0, V = 0$
LT	Less Than	$N = 1, V = 0$ or $N = 0, V = 1$
GT	Greater Than	$N = V = 1, Z = 0$ or $N = V = Z = 0$
LE	Less or Equal	$Z = 0$ or $N = 1, V = 0$ or

		N = 0, V = 1
T	True	Test result = 1
F	False	Test result = 0

In the Scc instruction the data byte is set to $ff if the test result is TRUE and to 0 if the test result is FALSE.

Interrupts

In the 68000 interrupts, both software and hardware are called exceptions. Seven levels of hardware interrupts can be triggered by applying a combination of inputs to the IPL0–IPL2 inputs. Level 7 is nonmaskable and has the highest priority with level 0 as the lowest priority. Note that these inputs use inverted logic so level 7 has all inputs at 0. The CPU also supports hardware generated vectors where the external device such as a 68901 MFP generates a vector address in response to the FC0-FC2 output for an interrupt acknowledge bus cycle. These vectors might typically be located in page 2 of the memory from $100–$1FF.

Software interrupts may be generated by one of sixteen TRAP instructions or by using the unimplemented $Axxx and $Fxxx opcodes. A number of other interrupts are generated by various system errors.

Exception vectors

In the 68000 the first 256 bytes of memory (locations 0–255) are used for storing the vector addresses for the exceptions. These are allocated as follows:

Vector No.	Hex. Address	Exception
0	000	SP after reset
1	004	PC after reset
2	008	Bus error
3	00C	Address error
4	010	ILLEGAL instruction
5	014	Division by zero
6	018	CHK instruction
7	01C	TRAPV instruction
8	020	Priviledge violation

9	024	Trace
10	028	$Axxx instruction code
11	02C	$Fxxx instruction code
12	030	Reserved
13	034	Reserved
14	038	Reserved
15	03C	Unitialized interrupt
16–23	040–05C	Reserved
24	060	Spurious interrupt
25	064	Level 1 interrupt
26	068	Level 2 interrupt
27	06C	Level 3 interrupt
28	070	Level 4 interrupt
29	074	Level 5 interrupt
30	078	Level 6 interrupt
31	07C	Level 7 interrupt (NMI)
32	080	TRAP #0
33	084	TRAP #1
34	088	TRAP #2
35	08C	TRAP #3
36	090	TRAP #4
37	094	TRAP #5
38	098	TRAP #6
39	09C	TRAP #7
40	0A0	TRAP #8
41	0A4	TRAP #9
42	0A8	TRAP #10
43	0AC	TRAP #11
44	0B0	TRAP #12
45	0B4	TRAP #13
46	0B8	TRAP #14
47	0BC	TRAP #15
48-63	0C0-0FC	Reserved

Exceptions 10 and 11 are generated by unimplemented instruction codes in the range $A000–$AFFF and $F000–$FFFF. By using these codes the processor can be given new instructions which it will execute as exceptions. Some computers, such as the Atari ST, use these instruction codes for producing graphics routines.

After a RESET the stack pointer is loaded from vector 0 and the program counter from vector 1.

The bus error exception is usually triggered because a device on the bus has not responded. After two successive bus errors the CPU switches to the HALT state.

Privilege violation is produced when the program

tries to access a protected part of the memory reserved for the system when the program is operating in user mode.

An address error is produced when the program tries to carry out a word or long operation at an odd address. All word and long data must be aligned at even addresses.

Motorola 68020

Although the 68000 has 32-bit internal architecture its effective speed is limited by the 16-bit data bus and the maximum memory is governed by the 24-bit address bus. The Motorola 68020 is an enhanced version which provides full 32-bit data and address buses.

The 68020 includes a 256-byte on-chip cache memory for instructions and a vector base register allows the exception vector table to be placed at any point in the memory map. The instruction set is compatible with that of the 68000 but includes additional instructions for bit field operations and for use with a 68881 or 68882 coprocessor.

Motorola 68030

This is an advanced 68000-type processor featuring full 32-bit architecture and bus systems. This processor includes on-chip cache memories for both data and instructions and has a built in memory management unit which permits virtual memory operation and multi-tasking to be carried out. In its user mode the 68030 provides the same set of internal registers as the basic 68000. When the 68030 is operating in supervisor mode it provides a number of additional control registers which handle the operation of the cache memories and the memory management system.

The 68030 instruction set is compatible with that of the 68000 but includes bit field operations and additional instructions for the internal MMU and an external coprocessor such as the 68881 or 68882.

7 RISC type processors

In the early days of microprocessors a major problem tended to be the limited amount of memory that could be provided for data and program storage. This was owing to the small capacity and high cost of available memory chips at that time. In order to reduce the amount of memory used by the program the approach adopted was to provide the CPU with a large number of different instructions many of which could perform complex operations such as multiplication. By using this wide range of instructions the amount of machine code needed and hence the amount of program memory could be reduced. For the more complex operations a single program opcode would trigger a hardware routine built into the CPU itself. This approach to microprocessor design is known as the complex instruction set computer (CISC) concept. All of the popular modern microprocessors, such as the Z80 and 68000, use this CISC design philosophy.

One disadvantage of the CISC design is that the CPU is much more complex and therefore the required chip is larger and more expensive to manufacture. A second problem is that the instructions take several cycles of CPU time for execution which reduces processing speed especially in programs which involve a large amount of calculation and little input–output activity.

An alternative design approach which has become popular in recent years is the reduced instruction set computer (RISC) design. In the RISC technique the number of instructions is reduced to those which are most frequently used in programs. The RISC processors normally have only two instructions, LOAD and STORE, which access the memory and the number of addressing modes provided is smaller than for a CISC machine. Most operations are carried out between registers within the CPU so RISC processors usually have a large bank of general purpose registers inside the CPU. An important design factor in RISC machines is that as far as possible instructions are designed to be executed in a single machine cycle. Thus execution can be very fast although the amount of program code and hence memory required is generally somewhat larger than for a CISC machine.

RISC processors are characterized by high instruction execution rates which are measured in millions of instructions per second (m.i.p.s.). They are particularly useful in calculation intensive programs which include a large number of repetitive operations. Typical applications might be in computer-aided design (CAD) workstations for updating complex graphics displays and in signal analysis or image processing. Although RISC chips are efficient at number crunching programs they tend to be slower when used for general-purpose computing where the CISC type processor may be more effective.

Sun SPARC

The SPARC (scalable processor architecture) chip was developed for Sun Microsystems and uses the Berkeley architecture developed by University of California at Berkeley. This 32-bit processor chip has 128 internal registers arranged in groups called windows. In the SPARC chip a window has eight IN registers, eight OUT registers and eight LOCAL registers. The adjacent windows overlap so that the OUT registers of one window act as the IN registers of the next window. The windows in the chip are arranged in an endless chain by linking the last window in the chain back to the first. In the SPARC processor there are 128 registers which produce a chain of eight windows. The CPU has only fifty basic instructions most of which need only one clock cycle for execution. To further speed up execution a pipeline technique is used where new instructions are fetched and decoded whilst the current instruction is being executed.

The CPU package is a 179 pin grid array type. Address and data buses are both 32-bits wide and a third 32-bit bus is provided for interfacing to a floating point coprocessor. The SPARC chip is currently being produced by Fujitsu and Cypress Semiconductor and LSI Logic. Typical execution rates are 10 m.i.p.s. for the Fujitsu chip and 20 m.i.p.s. for the Cypress CMOS version.

MIPS R2000/R3000

An alternative RISC scheme called the Stanford architecture was developed at Stanford University, California and is used in the R2000 chip manufactured initially by MIPS Computer Systems Inc. Several other manufacturers including LSI Logic, Integrated Device Technology and Siemens are now producing these chips under licence from MIPS.

The R2000 chip contains two processors, one used as the main CPU and the second handling address generation and memory accesses. The main processor has thirty-two general purpose registers of 32-bits each, two further 32-bit registers for multiply/divide and a 32-bit program counter. It has a set of fifty-eight instructions most of which execute in one clock cycle. The system coprocessor deals with memory management and interrupts. It has its own set of sixteen instructions which it detects from the main instruction stream and executes as appropriate. The R2000 supports two external cache memories, one for instructions and the other for data. A 32-bit data bus is used and the 32-bit address bus allows up to 4G bytes to be accessed.

The 12 MHz clock version of the R2000 can provide a processing speed of around 8 m.i.p.s. whilst the 16 MHz version gives around 10 m.i.p.s. The R2000 is built into a 144 pin grid array package. An R2010 floating point coprocessor can be added to speed up floating point calculations.

The R3000 processor is an enhanced version of the R2000 which gives a higher execution speed. The 16 MHz R3000 delivers some 12 m.i.p.s. whilst the 25 MHz version can produce 20 m.i.p.s. The R3000 is supplied in a 176 lead ceramic flat package. For fast floating point operations the R3010 floating point coprocessor can be added.

Motorola 88000

Motorola's 88000 RISC processor uses the Harvard architecture which has two separate bus systems, one being used for instructions and the other for data. There are four separate execution units in the CPU. The FP unit handles all floating point arithmetic operations and any conversions between FP and integer formats. The integer unit handles all integer arithmetic and logic operations. Each of these units has an associated bank of sixty-four registers which are 32-bits wide. The processor also has a bank of thirty-two general purpose 32-bit registers. The instruction and data units control memory access for instructions and data.

The 88000 is linked to the memory by two bus systems. The bus system for data has a 30-bit address and 32-bit data bus whilst a similar but separate bus system is used for transferring instruction codes. For maximum processing speed these two buses would be fed from cache memory units which in turn would access the main memory system.

Inmos transputer

The transputer developed by Inmos is a RISC type processor specifically designed for high-speed parallel processing and is available in both 16- and 32-bit versions. The basic internal architecture of the transputer is shown in Figure 61. An important feature of the transputer is the facility to link a number of devices together into an array. This is achieved by using high-speed serial link interfaces on the transputer chip. These links are designed to operate at 10M bits per second to provide rapid data transfer between transputers.

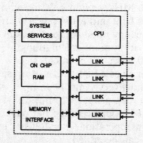

Figure 61 Block diagram of a T414 transputer

The central processing unit is supported by a system services module and a block of high-speed static RAM and an interface to access external memory. The transputer chip also includes a timer which runs from the system clock. The CPU itself normally contains eight registers.

The transputer uses a reduced instruction set (RISC) for programming although the actual machine code instruction set may vary from one type of transputer to another. The general philosophy adopted by Inmos is that programming should be carried out using Occam which is a high-level language designed for parallel processing applications. Thus, providing the appropriate compiler is used, there is no need for the programmer to know about the individual machine language instructions.

The serial data links transmit 1 byte at a time in a similar fashion to an asynchronous serial link. Each link has separate lines for sending and receiving. Each packet of data consists of two 1 bits followed by the eight data bits and terminated by a 0 bit. Receipt of the data is acknowledged by the remote device sending a 2-bit code back on the sending device's input line.

For parallel data input or output a C001 link adapter may be connected to one of the link interfaces of the transputer. This converts from the serial link to provide an 8-bit output port and an 8-bit input port. An alternative link adapter type C002 can be used to convert from the serial link to an 8-bit wide parallel bidirectional data bus. This would allow the transputer to be linked to a conventional 8-bit microprocessor bus system.

A typical transputer is the T414 which has a 32-bit bus system, 2k bytes of on-chip static RAM and four serial link interfaces. It is housed in an 84-pin J lead ceramic chip carrier and operates from a +5 V power supply.

Novix NC4016

This RISC type processor uses a stack orientated architecture and is specifically designed to execute FORTH primitive instructions directly. By using a multiple bus structure the NC4016 can carry out several operations simultaneously and can achieve very high processing speeds.

The basic organization of the NC4000 CPU is shown in Figure 62. Unlike other processors the NC4016 has three separate data and address bus systems. One of these provides 16-bit wide address and data paths to access the main memory. A second 16-bit data bus (S0–S15) with its associated 8-bit address bus (K0–K7) controls a separate memory which acts as the data stack. The top two words of this data stack are held in two internal registers of the CPU itself. These are the top (T) and next (N)

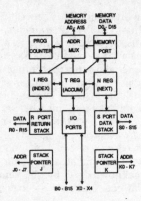

Figure 62 Internal layout of the Novix NC4016

registers. The T register is connected to the ALU and acts in much the same way as the accumulator in other processors.

The third 16-bit data bus (R0– R15) and its associated 8-bit address bus (J0–J7) control the return stack which also uses a separate memory. The data for the top word of this stack is held in a return index register (I).

There are also two input output ports (B and X). The B port provides a full 16-bit wide bidirectional I–O port which can be used for general input–output. The X port is only 5-bits wide and is intended to provide an extension to the main memory address to allow up to 4M bytes of main memory to be accessed. The X register can also be used for simple input–output if the extended memory is not required.

All instructions for the NC4000 are executed in one instruction cycle which, with an 8 MHz CPU clock, permits an execution rate of 8 m.i.p.s.

The NC4016 is packaged in a 120-lead pin grid array package.

Signal functions

CLK	CPU clock (any frequency up to 8 MHz)
A0–A15	Main memory address bus
D0–D15	Main memory data bus
K0–K7	Data stack address bus
S0–S15	Data stack data bus
J0–J7	Return stack address bus

R0–R15	Return stack data bus
B0–B15	Input–output port B
X0–X5	Input–output port X
WEH	Write enable for memory MSB
WEL	Write enable for memory LSB
WES	Write enable for data stack memory
WER	Write enable for return stack memory
WEB	Write enable for I/O ports B and X
RST	Reset input
Vdd	+5 V power supply
Vss	Ground 0 V

The X4 input on the X port can also be programmed to operate as an interrupt input.

Instruction set

Unlike the other types of processor the NC4000 executes FORTH instructions directly so the compiler simply converts each FORTH primitive instruction into its equivalent binary instruction word for the NC4016. Instructions implemented corresponding to single FORTH words are:

DUP	Duplicate top item on stack
DROP	Drop top item from stack
OVER	Make copy of N to top of stack
SWAP	Swap contents of T and N
+	Add top two words on stack
+c	As + but with carry
−	Subtract T from N
−c	As − but with carry
OR	Logical OR
AND	Logical AND
XOR	Logical XOR
2/	Arithmetic shift right 1-bit
2*	Arithmetic shift left 1-bit
0<	Test for zero
D2/	Double length ASR by 1-bit
D2*	Double length ASL by 1-bit
*'	Multiply step
*_	Signed multiply step
*F	Fractional multiply step
/'	Divide step
/"	Last divide step
S'	Square root step
R>	Pop return stack top to data stack
R@	Copy return stack top to data stack

#I	Copy index to data stack
>R	Push data stack top to return stack
IF	Jump if T=0
ELSE	Jump
#LOOP	Jump and decrement loop count if <>0
TIMES	Set loop counter
CALL	Jump to subroutine
EXIT	Return from subroutine
@	Load data from memory
!	Store data to mcmory
I@	Load data from internal register
I!	Store data to internal register

Apart from memory accesses which take two cycles, these instructions execute in one machine cycle. In many cases two, three or four FORTH words can be executed simultaneously as a single instruction during a single clock cycle. When memory or I/O ports are accessed an extra clock cycle is required. Taking these combinations into account the processor can execute about 170 different instructions.

Acorn RISC machine (ARM)

This chip was developed by Acorn Computer for use in their Archimedes computer and for dedicated workstations. This reduced instruction set computer (RISC) processor has been implemented by VLSI Technology Inc. with the type number VL86C010.

This processor has 32-bit internal architecture with a full 32-bit data bus and a 26-bit address bus which permits 64M bytes of directly addressed memory. There are some thirty basic instructions but some may be combined into a single operation and there are a wide selection of addressing options. Many instructions take just one machine cycle but timing tends to be complicated because the processor uses a pipeline system in which the opcode fetch and decode operations for the following instructions are carried out whilst the current instruction executes.

The processor is package in a 84-pin plastic leaded chip carrier (PLCC) and pin connections are shown in Figure 63.

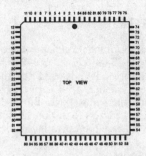

PIN	SIGNAL	PIN	SIGNAL	PIN	SIGNAL
1	CLK O2	29	A13	57	D9
2	CLK O1	30	A12	58	D10
3	-R/W	31	A11	59	D11
4	-OPC	32	Vcc	60	D12
5	-MREQ	33	GND	61	D13
6	ABORT	34	A10	62	D14
7	-IRQ	35	A9	63	D15
8	-FIRQ	36	A8	64	D16
9	RESET	37	A7	65	D17
10	-TRAN	38	A6	66	D18
11	Vcc	39	A5	67	D19
12	CPB	40	A4	68	D20
13	-M1	41	A3	69	D21
14	-M0	42	A2	70	D22
15	SEQ	43	A1	71	D23
16	ALE	44	A0	72	D24
17	A25	45	ABE	73	D25
18	A24	46	D0	74	D26
19	A23	47	D1	75	GND
20	A22	48	D2	76	CPA
21	A21	49	D3	77	D27
22	A20	50	D4	78	D28
23	A19	51	D5	79	D29
24	A18	52	D6	80	D30
25	A17	53	D7	81	D31
26	A16	54	GND	82	-CPI
27	A15	55	Vcc	83	DBE
28	A14	56	D8	84	-B/W

Figure 63 Pin connections for Acorn ARM CPU

Signal lines

D0–D31	Data bus (bidirectional)
A0–A25	Address bus (output)
DBE	Data bus enable (input)
ABE	Address bus enable (input)
ALE	Address latch enable (input)
M0–M1	Mode (output)
RES	Reset input
ABRT	Abort input
IRQ	Interrupt request (input)
FIRQ	Fast interrupt request (input)
R/W	Read/write (output)
MREQ	Memory request (output)
TRANS	Translate enable (output)
OPC	Opcode fetch (output)
SEQ	Next address sequential (output)
CPI	Coprocessor instruction (output)
CPB	Coprocessor busy (input)
CPA	Coprocessor absent (input)

Internal registers

Under normal user mode conditions there are sixteen general-purpose 32-bit registers R0–R15 available to the user. Of these, R15 is used for the program counter (PC) and status (PSR). In this register bits 26–31 provide the status flags. Bits 2–25 give the program counter address (based on 32-bit words) and bits 0 and 1 indicate the operating mode.

Operating modes

Bit 1	Bit 0	Mode
0	0	User program
0	1	FIRQ interrupt
1	0	IRQ interrupt
1	1	Supervisor program

During FIRQ interrupts seven private registers (R8__firq–R14__firq) may be used to save a return address and other register data. For IRQ interrupts two private registers (R13__irq and R14__irq) are available whilst for the supervisor mode two private registers (R13__svc and R14__svc) may be used.

Status bits

Bit	Flag	Function
26	F	FIRQ mask bit
27	I	IRQ mask bit
28	V	Overflow bit
29	C	Carry bit
30	Z	Zero bit
31	N	Sign bit

Instruction set

ADC	Add with carry
ADD	Add
SBC	Subtract with carry
SUB	Subtract
RSB	Reverse subtract
RSC	Reverse subtract with carry
MUL	Multiply

MLA	Multiply and add
AND	Logical AND
ORR	Inclusive OR
EOR	Exclusive OR
CMP	Compare
CMN	Compare negative
MOV	Move
MVN	Move negative
BIC	Bit clear
TEQ	Test for equality
TST	Test masked
B	Branch
BL	Branch with link (subroutine call)
ASR	Arithmetic shift right
LSL	Logic shift left
LSR	Logic shift right
ROR	Rotate right
LDR	Load memory to register
STR	Store register to memory
LDM	Load multiple registers
STM	Store multiple registers
SWI	Software interrupt

Condition codes

All instructions can be specified as conditional by adding in the condition code as follows:

EQ	Equal $Z = 1$
NE	Not equal $Z = 0$
CS	Carry set $C = 1$
CC	Carry clear $C = 0$
MI	Minus $N = 1$
PL	Plus $N = 0$
VS	Overflow set $V = 1$
VC	Overflow clear $V = 0$
HI	Higher $C = 1$, $Z = 0$
LS	Lower or same ($C = 0$, $Z = 1$)
GE	Greater or equal ($N = V = 1$) or ($N = V = 0$)
LT	Less than ($N = 1$, $V = 0$) or ($N = 0$, $V = 1$)
LE	Less or equal ($Z = N = 1$, $V = 0$) or ($N = 0$, $V = 1$)
AL	Always
NV	Never

Address modes

Most operations are carried out between registers to give high execution speed with load and store operations as required to transfer data to and from memory. Memory addressing includes absolute, base address relative, PC relative, pre-incremented or decremented and post-incremented or decremented.

Support devices

The ARM processor is one of a set of related chips which can be used to form a powerful microcomputer system. The other support chips are:

VL86C110   Memory controller. Provides memory and bus management.

VL86C310   Video controller. A versatile video generator giving a wide range of screen resolutions and up to 4096 colours. Also includes a sound generation system.

VL86C410   I/O controller. This provides an interface between the fast data bus of the ARM CPU and a slower I/O bus suitable for driving standard I/O devices. The controller contains four timers and provides a serial keyboard interface.

8 Single chip computers

The usual general-purpose microprocessor chip, such as the Z80, 6809 or 6502, whilst being very flexible does require a number of additional chips added to it in order to produce a working microcomputer system. The additional chips usually consist of memory devices for program and data storage and also input and output ports to allow the CPU to communicate with the external world. Without these added chips the microprocessor is totally useless. For simple applications such as in domestic appliances or simple industrial controllers only a small amount of memory is actually needed to perform the desired task and the number of I–O channels is similarly relatively small. To simplify the design of such equipment a number of devices have been produced which include not only the CPU but some memory and I–O facilities on a single integrated circuit chip. Such devices are usually referred to as single chip microcomputers or microcontrollers. By using such a device the circuit board may be made quite simple with just a few passive components around the microcontroller and perhaps a few transistors to drive indicators or displays where these need more current or voltage than the microcontroller chip can handle.

Intel 8048/49 series

This series of microcomputers has an 8-bit internal data bus and the various devices in series provide a selection of options in terms of size of RAM and ROM and the configuration of the input and output ports. There are also CMOS versions available with type numbers in the 80C48 series.

The 12-bit program counter can address up to 4k bytes of program arranged in two banks of 2k bytes. Normally 1 or 2k bytes of internal ROM may be provided. Some devices such as the 8648 and 8748 contain programmable ROMs whilst the 8039 has no internal ROM.

An internal RAM of 64 or 128 bytes is provided and this is used for working registers, a data stack and storage space for variables. This RAM is addressed by using a RAM pointer register which is accessed via the data bus. The RAM pointer being 8-bit can address up to 256 bytes of RAM and may be used to address external RAM by feeding its contents out via an output port to provide an external address bus.

An 8-bit accumulator provides arithmetic and logic operations in conjuction with an 8-bit status register. There is also an 8-bit timer register provided in the CPU. For input and output these devices have three ports providing up to twenty-eight input and output lines and the 8022 includes an A/D converter for analogue input.

The interrupt system is quite simple. External interrupts are fed in via the INT input and a jump is made to the instruction at program memory address 3. An interrupt can also be triggered by the timer and this causes a jump to program address 7. A processor reset causes a jump to program address 0.

A point to note in the instruction set is that there is no SUBTRACT instruction. This function can, however, be provided by using the NEGATE instruction on the number to be subtracted and then using the ADD instruction.

The package for the 8048 series is a 40-pin DIL type and pin connections are compatible although some processors vary slightly in pin functions. The connections for the 8048 are shown in Figure 64.

T0	1	40	Vcc
X1	2	39	T1
X2	3	38	P27
RES	4	37	P26
SS	5	36	P25
INT	6	35	P24
EA	7	34	P17
RD	8	33	P16
PSEN	9	32	P15
WR	10	31	P14
ALE	11	30	P13
DB0	12	29	P12
DB1	13	28	P11
DB2	14	27	P10
DB3	15	26	Vdd
DB4	16	25	PROG
DB5	17	24	P23
DB6	18	23	P22
DB7	19	22	P21
GND	20	21	P20

Figure 64 Pin connections for the 8048 MCU

Signal functions

DB0–DB7	Data bus or bidirectional port
P10–P17	Port 1 quasi-bidirectional
P20–P27	Port 2 quasi-bidirectional
PRG	Output strobe for 8243 expander
T0–T1	Testable inputs
XTAL1,XTAL2	Timing crystal input
EA	External access input
SS	Single step input
RD	Read strobe output
WR	Write strobe output
ALE	Address latch enable output
INT	Interrupt input
PSEN	Program store enable output
RESET	Reset input
Vdd	Battery backup supply for 8048, 8035L
	+25 V (program) or +5 V for 8648, 8748

Power supply (8048) Vcc = +4.75 V to +5.25 V at 135 mA.

Connections for the 8049 and 8039 are the same as for 8048.

Instruction set

Data transfer

MOV A,#data	Load A immediate with data
MOV A,r	Move r to A
MOV A,@r	Move indirect memory (r) to A
MOV A,PSW	Move PSW to A
MOV r,#data	Move immediate data to register r
MOV r,A	Move A to r
MOV @r,A	Move A indirect to memory (r)
MOV r,#data	Move data indirect to memory (r)
MOV PSW,A	Move A to PSW
MOVP A,@A	Move data from current page to A
MOVP3 A,@A	Move data from page 3 to A
MOVX A,@r	Move indirect external memory to A
MOVX @r,A	Move A indirect to external memory

MOVD A,Pp	Move data from port P4–P7 to A
MOVD Pp,A	Move data from A to port P4–P7
MOV A,T	Move timer data to A
MOV T,A	Move A to timer
XCH A,r	Exchange A with r
XCH A,@r	Exchange A indirect with memory (r)
IN A,Pp	Input from port p to A
INS A,BUS	Input BUS data to A
OUTL BUS,A	Output A to BUS
OUT Pp,A	Output A to port P1 or P2

Arithmetic

ADD A.r	Add register to A
ADD A,@r	Add indirect to A
ADD A,#data	Add immediate data to A
ADDC A,@r	Add with carry register r
ADDC A,r	Add indirect with carry
ADDC A,#data	Add immediate data with carry
DAA	Decimal adjust A
DEC A	Decrement A
DEC Rr	Decrement register r
INC A	Increment A
INC Rr	Increment register r
INC Rr	Increment indirect memory (r)

Logic

ANL A,r	AND A with register r
ANL A,@r	AND A indirect
ANL A,#data	AND A immediate with data
ANL BUS,#data	AND data with Bus
ANL Pp,#data	AND Port P1 or P2 with data
ANLD Pp,#data	AND Port P4-P7 with data
ORL A,r	OR A with r
ORL A,@r	OR A indirect
ORL A,#data	OR A immediate with data
ORL BUS,#data	OR BUS with data
ORL Pp,#data	OR port P1 or P2 with data
ORLD Pp,#data	OR port P4-P7 with data
XRL A,r	EXCLUSIVE OR A with r
XRL A,@r	EXCLUSIVE OR A indirect

XRL A #data	EXCLUSIVE OR A immediate with data
CLR A	Clear A to zero
CLR C	Clear carry flag
CLR F0	Clear flag F0
CLR F1	Clear flag F1
CPL A	Complement A
CPL C	Complement carry flag
CPL F0	Complement flag F0
CPL F1	Complement flag F1
RL A	Rotate left A by 1-bit
RLC A	Rotate left A through carry
RR A	Rotate right A
RRC A	Rotate right A through carry

Branch and jump

CALL addr	Call subroutine
JZ addr	Jump if A = 0
JNZ addr	Jump if A is not 0
JBb addr	Jump if bit b in A is set
JC addr	Jump if carry flag = 1
JNC addr	Jump if carry flag = 0
JMP addr	Jump to address
JMPP @A	Jump indirect within current page
JTF addr	Jump if timer flag is set
JT0 addr	Jump if T0 = 1
JT1 addr	Jump if T1 = 1
JNI addr	Jump if INT input = 0
JNT0 addr	Jump if T0 = 0
JNT1 addr	Jump if T1 = 0
JF0 addr	Jump if F0 flag is set
JF1 addr	Jump if f1 flag is set
DJNZ Rr,addr	Decrement r and jump if r not zero

Miscellaneous

EN I	Enable interrupt
EN TCNTI	Enable timer interrupt
DIS I	Disable interrupt
DIS TCNTI	Disable timer interrupt
RET	Return from subroutine
RETR	Return from S/R and restore PSW

SEL RB0	Select register bank 0
SEL RB1	Select register bank 1
SEL MB0	Select memory bank 0
SEL MB1	Select memory bank 1
ENT0 CLK	Enable clock output to T0
STOP TCNT	Stop timer/counter
STRT T	Start count for timer
NOP	No operation

The instructions for input and output to BUS allow the data bus lines DB0–DB7 to be used as a bidirectional input–output port.

Intel 8051 series

These devices have a similar internal organization to the 8048 types except that the program counter and RAM pointer registers are both 16-bits wide thus allowing up to 64k of ROM and 64k of RAM. Four 8-bit I–O ports are provided. When external RAM and ROM are used ports 0 and 1 carry the address bus signals and port 2 acts as the external data bus. The internal RAM is normally 128 bytes whilst the ROM for the 8051 is 4k bytes. A programmable ROM is provided in the 8751 and the 8031 has no internal ROM. Two 16-bit timers are included on the chip and there is also a UART to provide serial input and output.

Figure 65 shows the pin connections for the 40-pin DIL package of the basic 8051.

When EA is low the CPU executes instructions from external memory whilst ALE (address latch enable) and PSEN (program store enable) are used to control the external memory. In this mode port 0 provides a multiplexed address/data bus and port 2 provides the high byte of the external address. Read/write control is via P36 (WR) and P37 (RD). With EA high the CPU executes the internal ROM program. The serial I/O uses P30 (RXD) and P31 (TXD).

The instruction set is different from that of the 8048 series and provides a set of 111 instructions.

Motorola 6801

This single chip microcomputer consists basically of a 6800 type CPU with 2k bytes of ROM and 128 bytes of RAM. Also included on the chip are four

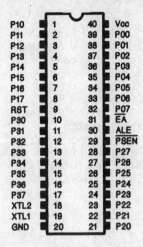

Figure 65 Pin connections for the 8051 MCU

input–output ports giving thirty-one parallel input–output lines, a serial input–output and a timer. A CMOS version of this microcomputer is the Hitachi 6301 which also supports a few additional instructions. Versions with erasable PROM instead of masked ROM have type numbers 68701 and 63701 respectively.

The pin connections for the 40-pin DIL package are shown in Figure 66.

Figure 66 Pin connections for the 6801 MCU

Signal lines

P10–P17	Port 1 input-output lines
P20–P24	Port 2 input-output lines
P30–P37	Port 3 input-output lines
P40–P47	Port 4 input-output lines
SC1, SC2	Strobe/control lines
X1, EX2	CPU clock timing crystal
E	Enable (system) clock output
IRQ	Interrupt input (active low)
NMI	Non-masked interrupt (active low)
RES	Reset input (active low)
Vsb	Standby supply for on chip RAM

Power supply Vcc = +4.75 V to +5.25 V at 240 mA

The 6801 has three modes of operation which are selected by the states of port 2-bits 0–2 when the CPU is reset.

Mode 1   Single chip mode

Ports 1, 3 and 4 are 8-bit parallel I/O and port 2 is used by the timer and serial I/O. SC1 acts as an input strobe and SC2 provides an output strobe for use with port 3.

Mode 2   Expanded mode

Port 1 is 8-bit parallel I/O. Port 2 is used by the timer and serial I/O or may be used for parallel I/O. Port 3 acts as a data bus for external devices. Port 4 outputs the CPU address lines A0–A7 for selecting external devices. SC1 acts as an address strobe output and SC2 becomes a R/W control line output. The devices addressed externally using Port 4 and SC1 will appear at addresses $100–$1FF in the CPU memory map.

Mode 3   Expanded multiplexed mode

In this mode port 3 acts as a multiplexed address/data bus. SC1 becomes an address strobe output to indicate that address bits A0–A7 are being output on Port 3. Port 4 now outputs the address bits A8–A15. Ports 1 and 2 operate in the same way as in mode 1.

Internal registers

The first 32 bytes of the address map are used by registers for the input–output ports and timer control as follows:

Address	Register
$00	Port 1 data direction
$01	Port 2 data direction
$02	Port 1 data register
$03	Port 2 data register
$04	Port 3 data direction
$05	Port 4 data direction
$06	Port 3 data register
$07	Port 4 data register
$08	Timer control/status
$09	Counter (MSB)
$0A	Counter (LSB)
$0B	Output compare (MSB)
$0C	Output compare (LSB)
$0D	Input capture (MSB)
$0E	Input capture (LSB)
$0F	Port 3 control/status
$10	Serial rate and mode
$11	Serial control/status
$12	Serial receive data
$13	Serial transmit data
$14	RAM control
$15–$1F	reserved

Serial port

The serial input–output uses port 2-bit 3 (P23) as the receive data input line and port 2-bit 4 (P24) as the transmit data output line. Port 2-bit 2 (P23) may also be used to output a serial clock signal if required. The control/status register bits have the functions:

Bit	Function
0	Wake up bit
1	Enable transmit output to P24
2	Enable transmitter interrupt
3	Enable receive input from P23
4	Enable receiver interrupt
5	Transmit data register empty

| 6 | Overrun or framing error |
| 7 | Receiver data ready |

Bits 5, 6 and 7 are status bits and are read only.

Data format of serial signal is one start bit, eight data bits and one stop bit.

Serial mode register

Bits 0 and 1 of this register select the clock division ratio from the CPU clock as follows:

Bit 1	Bit 0	Clock ratio
0	0	1/16
0	1	1/128
1	0	1/1024
1	1	1/4096

When bit 3 is set at 1 it enables port line P22 for clock output (bit 2 = 0) or clock input (bit 2 = 1). When an external clock is used via P22 its frequency should be eight times the desired baud rate. If bits 3 and 4 are both 0 the transmitted signal is in biphase format. Other bit combinations produce the normal NRZL format.

The timer consists of a free running 16-bit counter which is incremented by the CPU clock. The contents of the output compare register ($0B/0C) are continually compared with the current counter data ($09/0A) and when a match occurs a flag is set in the timer status/control register. At the same time the state of bit 0 (output level) of the timer status/control register ($08) may be output to port 2-bit 1 (P21). When an input edge is applied to port 2-bit 0 (P20) the current value of the counter is transferred to the input capture register ($0D/0E). The timer control/status register bit functions are:

Bit	Function
0	Output level for P21
1	Active edge at P20 input (0 = high/low)
2	Enable timer overflow interrupt
3	Enable output compare interrupt
4	Enable unput capture interrupt
5	Timer overflow flag (count = 0000)
6	Output compare flag (compare

| | reg = count) |
| 7 | Input capture flag (edge detected at P20) |

Bits 5, 6 and 7 are read only.

The internal 128 byte RAM is located at addresses $0080–$00FF and the internal ROM or EPROM is located at addresses $F800–$FFFF. In the expanded multiplexed mode the remainder of the address map may be used for external memory or peripheral devices.

Instruction set

The basic instruction set is the same as for the 6800/6802 CPU with the following additional instructions.

LDD	Load ACCD with a 16-bit word
STD	Store ACCD to memory (16-bits)
PSHX	Push X register to stack
PULX	Pull X register from stack
ADDD	16-bit add to ACCD
SUBD	16-bit subtract from ACCD
ABX	Add ACCB to index register X
ASLD	Arithmetic shift left ACCD
LSRD	Logic shift right ACCD

Here ACCD is the double accumulator made up from ACCA and ACCB treated as a single 16-bit register with ACCA as the most significant byte.

Interrupts

The 6801 has several additional interrupt vectors to handle the on chip ports and timer/counter. The layout of the interrupt vectors at the top of the memory map is:

Address	Interrupt vector
$FFFE/FFFF	Restart (RES)
$FFFC/FFFD	Non masked interrupt (NMI)
$FFFA/FFFB	Software interrupt
$FFF8/FFF9	IRQ or input strobe (SC1)
$FFF6/FFF7	Timer input capture
$FFF4/FFF5	Timer output compare
$FFF2/FFF3	Timer overflow
$FFF0/FFF1	Serial I/O interrupt

142

Interrupt priority has restart as the highest level and serial I/O as the lowest level.

Motorola 6805 and 146805

The 6805 microcomputer chip is effectively a 6800 type CPU with a built in ROM for a dedicated program and a small amount of working RAM combined with three I/O ports to provide twenty input–output lines. There is also a built in timer. The internal bus structure consists of a 16-bit address bus and an 8-bit data bus as for the 6800 CPU. In the standard 6805 there are 1100 bytes of ROM and a 64 byte RAM. A number of variants of the 6805 provide a range of different configurations of input–output ports, RAM, and ROM including some versions with a built in EPROM.

The 146805 series are CMOS versions of the 6805 type microcomputer and come in a variety of different configurations.

Zilog Z8 series

These microcomputers contain 2k, 4k or 8k of ROM or EPROM, two counter-timers, a UART for serial I/O and a set of four input–output ports. A bank of 128 or 256 internal registers provide a register file of 124 or 236 general-purpose registers and the data, control and status registers for the timers and I/O channels. The instruction set consists of forty-seven basic operations some of which have a number of different addressing modes. The I/O ports can also be used to provide memory expansion by using up to 62k of external memory.

Some of the Z8 types available are:

Type	ROM	Reg. file	I/O lines	Package
Z8600	2k	124	22	28 DIL
Z8601	2k	124	32	40 DIL
Z8610	4k	124	22	28 DIL
Z8611	4k	124	32	40 DIL
Z8620	8k	236	22	28 DIL
Z8621	8k	236	32	40 DIL

The Z86E11 and Z86E21 are EPROM versions of the 8611, 8621.

The Z8671 is a Z8611 with Tiny BASIC in ROM.

The Z8681 is a version of the Z8601 with no ROM.

Figure 67 shows the pin allocation for the forty lead versions. In the forty lead types all four ports are 8-bits wide. Port 0 can be programmed as a pair of 4-bit wide channels which may be set as inputs or outputs. Port 1 can be set as either eight inputs or eight outputs. On port 2 each line can be individually set as either an input or output. Port 3 has its lower four bits permanently set as inputs and the upper 4 bits as outputs.

Vcc	1	40	P36
XTL2	2	39	P31
XTL1	3	38	P27
P37	4	37	P26
P30	5	36	P25
$\overline{RES}$	6	35	P24
R/$\overline{W}$	7	34	P23
$\overline{DS}$	8	33	P22
$\overline{AS}$	9	32	P21
P35	10	31	P20
GND	11	30	P33
P32	12	29	P34
P00	13	28	P17
P01	14	27	P16
P02	15	26	P15
P03	16	25	P14
P04	17	24	P13
P05	18	23	P12
P06	19	22	P11
P07	20	21	P10

Figure 67 Pin connections for Z8601, Z8611 MCU

The CPU can execute instructions from an external memory system and uses Port 1 as a multiplexed address/data bus whilst Port 0 provides the high order byte of the address. An address strobe (AS) output and data strobe (DS) together with a read/write (R/W) line are used to control the external memory.

The instruction set comprises forty-seven basic types of instruction and offers six addressing modes.

9 Parallel input and output

The simplest form of data output scheme is to transfer complete data words in parallel from the main data bus of the microprocessor system to the external device. The important thing that must be remembered here is that the desired data will only be presented on the data bus for a short period of time whilst the data transfer instruction is executed. To produce a useful output signal the data should remain available on the output lines until the external device has accepted it. This is achieved by transferring the bit pattern from the CPU data bus into a latch or output register which consists of a flip-flop stage for each bit of the data word. After the data transfer from the bus the data is held in the register until a new data transfer is made to it. The outputs from the register then drive the output lines as shown in Figure 68.

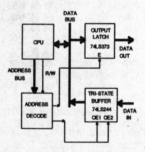

Figure 68 Parallel input–output using discrete logic

To perform an output operation the CPU places the desired data word on to the data bus and this is transferred into the output latch whilst the data bus signal is stable. Some processors have a special instruction such as OUT which performs this task. A control line outputs a signal to indicate that the data transfer is to an output port and this signal could be used as a clock for the output latch. If there are several output devices connected to the system then data from the CPU address bus may be used to indicate which device is to accept the data. In this case each output channel must decode the address data so that it responds only when its address is present.

Processors such as the Motorola 6800 series and the 6500 series devices treat all data transfers as memory read or write operations. In this case the input or output channels are simply allocated a memory address and treated as if they were part of the memory system. Thus to output data to an external device a simple STORE or MOVE instruction is used and the address is that allocated to the particular output channel.

Input signals may be treated in a similar way. In this case the input signal passes through a tristate gate to the main data bus. The gate is selected only when the appropriate input–output channel address is present on the address bus and data is then transferred via the data bus to the CPU. In simpler systems part of the available memory address space is allocated to input–output devices and no memory chips are included in this address area. In systems where the memory extends over the entire address range the addressing circuits for the input–output channels can be used to generate a signal which disables the memory when an input–output data transfer is being performed.

Although simple logic gates or latches can provide input or output channels for a microprocessor system there are a number of specially developed chips available for this purpose. These devices usually provide two or more 8-bit wide data channels which can be programmed to operate as either inputs or outputs. In most of these chips the individual lines of each port can be set up independently as inputs or outputs by writing a pattern of bits to control registers in the chip. These chips also provide facilities for detecting a change of input on some lines which can tell the CPU that data is required to be input or output.

Address decoding

In most microprocessor systems the input and output channels are treated as if they were locations in memory and the usual practice is to set aside a part of the memory address space for input–output channels. The layout of the various areas of the address space in a microcomputer system is generally referred to as the memory map and a system which treats input–output devices as if they were memory is called a 'memory mapped' I/O system.

For a typical 8-bit personal computer system the 64k byte address space might be allocated as shown in Figure 69. Here 16k bytes at the top of memory are allocated to ROM which will contain the operating system and any other regularly used programs. The next lower 16k bytes are allocated for input and output channels and the bottom 32k bytes of memory are used for RAM.

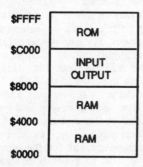

Figure 69 Simple example of a memory map

Address decoding logic must be arranged so that the ROM, RAM or I/O devices are activated only when a valid address in their particular area of the memory map is on the address bus. Other signals which must be taken into account are the read/write control and any strobe lines which determine the direction and timing of data transfers across the data bus. In the simple case shown in Figure 69 the basic address decoding is achieved by using a simple one to eight line decoder such as the 74LS138 as shown in Figure 70. This circuit assumes that the processor is a 6502 where the memory address is valid when the phase 2 clock signal CLK is high. The top two bits of the address are decoded and four outputs of the chip are used to select the four 16k areas of the memory map.

The R/W control line is fed directly to the RAM chips and the I/O circuits to switch their data in the appropriate direction on the data bus. Where simple gates and flip-flops are used as input–output channels the input gates are enabled only when the R/W signal is set at read whilst output flip-flops are activated during a write condition. In both cases the I/O circuit should only be connected to the bus when its address

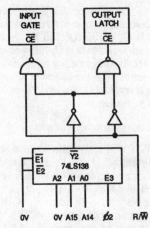

Figure 70 Simple address decoding scheme

is also activated.

In the case of the RAM the chip select (CS) lines are selected by outputs from the decoder and address bits A0–A13 are fed to the memory chip address inputs and used to select individual bytes in the selected memory bank. The R/W control is used to activate the write enable (WE) line when a write operation is executed. The ROM chips will have their output enable (OE) and chip select lines activated only when a read operation is performed.

If several I/O devices are connected these may be individually addressed by using the lower order address bits to select the appropriate I/O channel. Alternatively, a second 74138 might be used to select the individual I/O channels. Here its E input would be driven from one of the outputs of the first decoder and lower order address bus bits could be used to select one of the eight decoded outputs which would then activate a selected I/O channel. Most of the dedicated peripheral chips have one or two extra chip select inputs which may be used with the lower order address bus lines to select the chip when an appropriate address appears on the bus.

In systems using the 6802 the VMA line should be gated with the phase 2 clock to ensure that the memory or I/O chip is activated only when a valid address is on the bus. The 8085 and Z80 processors can address I/O devices directly when the IN or OUT data transfer instructions are used. In this case the lower 8-bits of the address bus provide an I/O channel address and a separate control line or lines (M/IO, MEMRQ, or IORQ) will be set to indicate whether the data transfer is with the memory or with an I/O channel. In this case the appropriate control line must be gated with the decoded address so that the I/O device responds only when it is required to perform a data transfer.

Intel 8255 PPI

For the Intel CPUs such as the 8085, 8086 etc., the 8255 is a programmable parallel peripheral interface (PPI) which can provide up to twenty-four input–output lines. Three 8-bit wide I/O ports are provided and each has its own data register. A fourth 8-bit register acts as a control register and determines the mode of operation of the chip. The 8255 has three different modes of operation.

In mode 0 the 8255 provides two 8-bit ports and two 4-bit ports. Each 8-bit port may be set as either eight inputs or eight outputs and similarly the 4-bit ports may be set as either four inputs or four outputs.

In mode 1 ports A and B operate as two independent 8-bit ports each of which may be set to give either eight input lines or eight output lines. The upper 4 bits of port C are now used as handshake lines for port A and the lower 4 bits of C provide handshake signals for port B.

In mode 2 the lines of port A can be individually set as inputs or outputs. In this mode port B acts as the data direction register and port C is used for handshake signals.

The 8255 comes in a 40-pin DIL package with connections as shown in Figure 71.

Signal lines

D0–D7	Data bus
CS	Chip select
RD	Read input
WR	Write input
A0–A1	Address inputs
RESET	Reset input
PA0–PA7	Port A I/O lines
PB0–PB7	Port B I/O lines
PC0–PC7	Port C I/O lines

Power supply Vcc $= +4.75$ V to $+5.25$ V at 120 mA

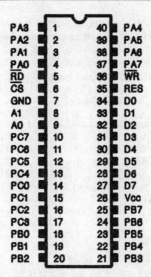

Figure 71 Pin connections for the 8255 PPI

Register selection

There are four addressable registers which are selected by the address inputs A0 and A1 as follows:

A1	A0	Register
0	0	Port A data register
0	1	Port B data register
1	0	Port C data register
1	1	Control register

The control register bits have the following action:

Bit	Function
0	Port C(L) direction (1 = input)
1	Port B direction (1 = input)
2	Port B mode (1 = mode 0)
3	Port C(H) direction (1 = input)
4	Port A direction (1-input)
5	Port A mode (1 = mode 0)
6	Selects mode 2 when at 1
7	Flag bit (selects bit set mode)

Here C(L) = bits 0–3 of port C and C(H) = bits 4–7 of port C.

When bit 7 of the control register is set the action of bits 0–3 of the control changes and becomes:

Bit 0   0 = reset bit   1 = set bit
Bits 1–3   select the bit to be set or reset

B3	B2	B1	Selected bit
0	0	0	PC0
0	0	1	PC1
0	1	0	PC2
0	1	1	PC3
1	0	0	PC4
1	0	1	PC5
1	1	0	PC6
1	1	1	PC7

In mode 1 when port A is set as an input bit 4 of C acts as an input strobe STBA which is active low. Bit C5 acts as a buffer full flag IBFA and is set when a strobe pulse is detected whilst bit C3 provides an interrupt output INTRA which may be fed to the CPU if interrupt operation is required. Bits C2, C1 and C0 provide the STBB, IBFB and INTRB signals for port B. The IBF flags are reset by reading port A or B data as appropriate.

When port A is set as an output then bit 7 of C acts as an output buffer full signal OBFA which is used to signal that data is ready. Bit C6 acts as an input for an acknowledge ACKA signal from the peripheral device and bit C3 again provides an interrupt output INTRA. For port B as an output bit C1 gives the OBFB signal, C2 acts as ACKB and C0 is again INTRB. The OBF flags are reset when a low is received on the associated ACK input.

6821 PIA

One versatile parallel port device designed for use with the 6800 processors is the 6821 peripheral interface adapter (PIA). The 6821 provides two complete 8-bit fully programmable parallel input–output ports PA and PB. It should be noted that the 6521 is an equivalent device from the 6500 series. This chip comes in a 40-lead dual in line package with connections as shown in Figure 72.

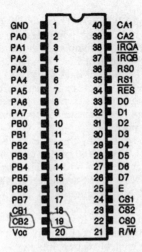

Figure 72 Pin connections for the 6821 PIA

Signal lines

D0–D7	Data bus lines
PA0–PA7	Port A input–output lines
PB0–PB7	Port B input–output lines
R/W	Read/write control input
CS0-2	Chip select inputs
RS0, RS1	Register select inputs
IRQA, IRQB	Interrupt outputs
CA1, CA2	Port A handshake lines
CB1, CB2	Port B handshake lines
RES	Reset input (active low)
E	Enable input

Power supply Vcc = +4.75 V to +5.25 V at 100 mA.

The enable input is usually derived from phase 2 of the CPU clock when data transfers are normally executed.

Internal registers

The 6821 contains six internal registers which are selected by the register select lines RS0 and RS1. Each port has three registers, one for data (PA, PB), one for data direction (DDRA, DDRB) and a control register (CRA, CRB).

Each data register provides eight input–output lines

(PA0–PA7 and PB0–PB7). The data direction register determines which of the port lines are inputs and which are outputs. A1 signifies output and 0 signifies input. Bits 0–7 control input–output lines 0 to 7 respectively. Four additional lines (CA1, CA2 and CB1, CB2) provide handshake signals for the two ports. Each port has its own control register which allows a variety of options to be programmed for the action of the port.

The port is selected by the state of RS1 (0 = Port A, 1 = Port B). When RS0 = 0 the control register is selected. Either the data or data direction register is selected when RS = 1. The actual register that is active is determined by the state of bit 2 in the control register for the port.

The control registers for ports A and B perform the same functions with each controlling its own port. Action of the control register bits is:

Bit	Function
CR0	Sets active edge for CA1 (CB1) input (0 = high/low 1 = low/high)
CR1	Interrupt enable for CA1 (CB1) input (0 = disabled 1 = enabled)
CR2	Selects data or data direction register (0 = direction 1 = data)
CR3	Selects active edge for CA2 (CB2) input (0 = high/low 1 = low/high)
CR4	Interrupt enable for CA2 (CB2) input (0 = disabled 1 = enabled)
CR5	Sets CA2 (CB2) as input or output (0 = input 1 = output)
CR6	Interrupt flag bit for CA1 (CB1)
CR7	Interrupt flag bit for CA2 (CB2)

When CA2 or CB2 has been set up as an output (CR5 = 1) and CR4 = 0 the CA2 or CB2 output takes up the state of control register bit CR3. When CR4 = 1 the actions of CA2 and CB2 are different. In this mode CA2 is set low after the A data register is read whilst CB2 is set low after a write to the B data register. In both cases if CR3 = 0 the state of CA2 (or CB2) returns high on the next active transition of CA1 (or CB1). When CR3 = 1, the CA2 or CB2 output returns high on the next enable pulse.

The flag bit CR6 is set when an active transition occurs on the CA1 (CB1) input and can be reset by reading the data register for the port. If the interrupt was enabled by CR1 then the output line IRQA (IRQB) will go low until the flag bit is cleared. With the interrupt disabled the flag bit is set in the control register but no IRQ output is produced. The flag bit CR7 works in the same way for CA2 (CB2) when that line is used as an input. If CA2 (CB2) is set as an output it has no effect on either CR7 or the IRQ output.

The RES input should normally be connected to main system reset line. After switch on or following a system reset the port will be initialized with all lines set up as inputs and all bits of the control register at 0. At this point the data direction register is selected and the appropriate bit pattern may be written to it to set up the I/O lines. Bit CR2 of the control register should then be set to 1 to select the port data register.

Zilog 8420 PIO

The 8420 is a parallel input–output chip designed for use in systems based around the Z80 CPU. It provides two 8-bit ports which can be programmed to provide various input–output configurations. The connections for its 40-pin DIL package are shown in Figure 73.

Figure 73 Pin connections for the 8420 PIO

Signal lines

A0–A7	Port A I/O lines
B0–B7	Port B I/O lines
D0–D7	Data bus lines
CE	Chip enable (active low)
RD	Read control (active low)
A/B	Port select
C/D	Register select
CLK	Clock input from CPU
INT	Interrupt input (active low)
IEI	Interrupt chain input
IEO	Interrupt chain out
IORQ	I/O request control (active low)
M1	M1 cycle signal from CPU
ASTB	Port A strobe input
BSTB	Port B strobe inputs
ARDY	Port A ready output
BRDY	Port B ready output

Power supply Vcc = +4.75 V to +5.25 V at 70 mA

For handshake purposes each port has a ready (RDY) line giving an output and a strobe (STB) as an input. There are also interrupt input (IEI) and output (IEO) lines to allow daisy chaining of interrupts as well as the INT line which provides an interrupt output generated by the 8420 itself.

Internal registers

Each port has a data register and a control register. Port A or port B registers are selected by the state of the AB input with port A selected when the input is at 0. The CD input similarly selects either the control or data register with the data register selected by CD = 0.

The 8420 has 4 modes of operation as follows:

Mode 0	Port set up as an 8-bit output
Mode 1	Port set up as an 8-bit input
Mode 2	Port A as input–output lines
	Port B as data direction register
Mode 3	Ports A and B programmable as I/O
	No handshaking facility

To set the mode of operation bits 0–3 of the control register are set at 1 and bits 6 and 7 are set to the desired mode number.

Centronics printer interface

One standard form of parallel interface is the Centronics version which is generally used for printers and plotters. This uses an Amphenol 36-way side contact connector.

Pin	Signal	Function
1	STROBE	Data Strobe (active low)
2	DATA1	Data bit 1 (LSB)
3	DATA2	Data bit 2
4	DATA3	Data bit 3
5	DATA4	Data bit 4
6	DATA5	Data bit 5
7	DATA6	Data bit 6
8	DATA7	Data bit 7
9	DATA8	Data bit 8 (MSB)
10	ACKNLG	Acknowledge (active low)
11	BUSY	Printer busy
12	PE	Paper end
13	SLCT	Select status of printer
14	AUTO XT	Auto line feed
15		no connection
16	GND	Logic ground
17	CHASSIS	Printer chassis
18		no connection
19	GND	Return line for pin 1
20	GND	Return line for pin 2
21	GND	Return line for pin 3
22	GND	Return line for pin 4
23	GND	Return line for pin 5
24	GND	Return line for pin 6
25	GND	Return line for pin 7
26	GND	Return line for pin 8
27	GND	Return line for pin 9
28	GND	Return line for pin 10
29	GND	Return line for pin 11
30	GND	Return line for pin 12
31	INIT	Initialize printer (active low)
32	ERROR	Error status line (active low)
33	GND	Signal ground
34		no connection
35	LOGIC1	
36	SLCT IN	Select input to printer

All signals are standard TTL logic levels although some printers include pull up resistors on signal inputs which may impose more than one TTL load on the input signal.

The original interface was designed to use twisted pair connections for the signals on pins 1 to 12 so separate return lines are provided on pins 19 to 30. Most systems, however, have pins 19 to 30 commoned together as a single ground return.

Many popular computer systems use only the signals on pins 1 to 12 and ignore all other signals although these may be provided on the printer.

Timing

The timing of the signals on a Centronics interface is shown in Figure 74. Assuming that the BUSY signal is at 0 the processor can set up data on the data lines and when this is stable a STROBE pulse is output. This strobe pulse should be at least 0.5 μs in duration. When the printer, or other peripheral unit, receives the strobe pulse it sets its BUSY line at 1 and after the data has been accepted it sends back an acknowledge pulse to indicate that the data may be changed. The BUSY line will normally be held high until the printer has completed its printing operation. If the printer has an input buffer memory then BUSY is reset to low after the acknowledge pulse has been sent unless the buffer is full.

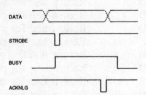

Figure 74 Signal timing on a Centronics interface

Some computer systems use only one of the status handshake signals ACKNLG and BUSY.

Direct memory access

Under normal operation the transfer of a block of data words from, say, the memory to an external device, such as a disk memory, has to be done one word at a time by first reading the word from the memory into a CPU register, such as the accumulator, and then writing the word out to the output device. Thus at least two instructions and several machine cycles are needed to transfer each word. Further instructions are also needed to keep track of the number of words transferred so that the operation can be terminated correctly.

It would be much better if the data could be transferred directly from the memory to the external device via the data bus without having to pass through the CPU at all. This can be done by using a special direct memory access (DMA) chip to control the data transfers instead of using the CPU. The DMA chip contains a simple counter which provides the address for the memory and a second counter keeps track of the number of words transferred. The DMA chip itself controls the operation of the address and data buses of the microprocessor system whilst the block of data words is transferred between the memory and the external device. In order for such a system to work the CPU must give up control of the address and data buses whilst the DMA operation is in progress otherwise there will be a conflict of signals on the bus wires.

When a DMA data transfer is to take place the CPU will first of all tell the DMA device how many words are to be transferred and the starting address to be used in the memory. This is done by writing the appropriate data to registers inside the DMA chip. When the external device signals to the DMA chip that it is ready to transfer data the DMA chip will output a DMA request signal. This is fed to the processor and will request access to the bus system. In some simple processor systems the HALT input is often used for this signal. The CPU now completes its current instruction and then releases the data and address buses and possibly some control lines such as R/W. The CPU then outputs a signal to show that it has released the bus and this is fed back to the DMA chip as a DMA grant signal. At this point the DMA device takes over the bus system and carries out the transfer of the block of data between the memory and the external device. When this operation is complete the DMA request signal is removed and the CPU again takes over control of the bus system.

The block of data transferred during DMA operations may be 256 bytes or more in length which will take up perhaps 256 or more clock cycles of the CPU timing. Some CPUs, however, cannot be held in the halted condition for this length of time without internal problems developing so an alternative form of DMA operation may be used. This alternative scheme is known as 'cycle stealing'. In this case the DMA device takes over the bus system for just one clock cycle and 1 byte is transferred. This can often be accommodated during a clock cycle where the CPU is not using the bus system. An example might be the phase 1 cycle in a 6802 CPU which only drives the bus system during its phase 0 cycle.

The main advantage of using a DMA system is that blocks of data can be transferred rapidly with the minimum interruption to program execution by the CPU.

The IEEE488 instrument bus

One parallel input–output system which is widely used for measuring instruments and test equipment is the IEEE488 general purpose instrument bus (GPIB). This bus system was originally developed by Hewlett Packard for linking their laboratory instruments to computers and was called the Hewlett Packard instrument bus (HPIB). The IEEE488 bus is now widely used in industrial control systems as well as in laboratory instrumentation.

The GPIB has three sets of bus lines. One set is the data bus which consists of eight bidirectional lines and is used to carry data and commands between the various devices connected to the bus. The second bus is the management bus which carries five control and status signals. These are ATN, EOI, IFC, REN and SRQ. The remaining three signal lines are used for handshaking between the devices on the bus and carry the signals NRFD, NDAC and DAV.

This bus uses a 24-way Amphenol side contact connector.

Signal connections

Pin	Abbreviation	Signal
1	DIO 1	Data bit 1 (LS)
2	DIO 2	Data bit 2
3	DIO 3	Data bit 3
4	DIO 4	Data bit 4
5	EOI	End or identify
6	DAV	Data valid

7	NRFD	Not ready for data
8	NDAC	Not data accepted
9	IFC	Interface clear
10	SRQ	Service request
11	ATN	Attention
12	SCRN	Screen
13	DIO 5	Data bit 5
14	DIO 6	Data bit 6
15	DIO 7	Data bit 7
16	DIO 8	Data bit 8
17	REN	Remote enable
18	GRND	Ground
19	GRND	Ground
20	GRND	Ground
21	GRND	Ground
22	GRND	Ground
23	GRND	Ground
24	GRND	Ground

ATN is asserted on the bus by the controller to indicate that a command is to be placed on the bus lines.

REN enables an instrument on the bus to be selected for remote control via the bus rather than from its own control panel.

SRQ is placed on the bus by an instrument which requires service.

EOI is sent by a talker to signify end of data and is used by the controller to request an instrument to identify itself.

IFC is placed on the bus by a controller to reset all instruments to a specified state.

Devices connected to the bus may act as either talkers when they send data to the bus lines or as listeners when they receive data from the bus lines. Only one device can act as talker at any time although several devices may be acting as listeners. One of the devices on the bus system also acts as the bus controller and governs the overall operation of the bus system.

Devices can be switched from being listeners to becoming talkers by sending commands along the data lines. It is also possible for the control of the bus to be transferred from the normal controller device to another device on the system if desired.

Each device on the bus can have its own address and up to thirty-one devices can be addressed. Device addresses are sent via the data bus as a parallel 7-bit word. The lowest 5-bits provide the device address whilst the next two bits provide control information. If these bits are both 0 the addressed device is switched to act as a listener. When the bit 5 is 1 and bit 6 is 0 the addressed device is switched to operate as a talker. If bit 6 is 1 and bit 5 is 0 the address data is treated as what is known as a secondary address. This may be used to perform some customized function in a previously addressed device. If both bit 5 and bit 6 are at 1 the data is treated as a command code.

When device address 31 is used as a talk or listen command it performs the function UNTALK or UNLISTEN and effectively switches off the talker or the currently selected listeners.

When a device has been selected as a talker it can send data words along the bus to all of the devices that are set up as listeners. This is done by the device setting the SRQ line low to request service. The controller then sends an ATN signal and will usually poll each device in turn to find out which one requires attention. The selected device is then set up as a talker and can send data to the bus.

A typical bus handshake sequence will start when the NRFD line is false indicating that all listeners are ready to accept a data word. When DAV goes true indicating that new data has been placed on the bus each device will set both NRFD and NDAC lines to true. As each device accepts the data it returns its NDAC line to false. When all devices have accepted the data the NDAC bus line will go to false and the talker may now change the data word on the bus. This new data word however will be ignored until all devices have signalled that they are ready for data. At this point the NDAC line will again go to true and the cycle repeats. When all of the data words have been sent the talker places a signal on the EOI line and the controller again takes over the bus.

Data on the bus is normally sent as ASCII characters and numbers are sent in decimal form as a sequence of numerical character codes. A carriage return code may be used to terminate a set of data instead of using the EOI line if desired. Text data may also be sent over the bus system in the same way.

The signals on the IEEE488 bus are usually logic level signals but the system is normally arranged as a wired OR configuration and the logic sense is reversed so that a high signal on the bus represents a data 0 or FALSE condition and a low signal is 1 or TRUE. In this bus system the logic states are usually referred to as TRUE or FALSE rather than 1 or 0.

Types of command

Command (binary)	Name	Function	Device affected
00000001	GTL	Go to local	Address
00000100	SDC	Selected device clear	Address
00000101	PPC	Parallel poll configure	Address
00001000	GET	Group enable trigger	Address
00010001	LLO	Local lockout	All
00010100	DCL	Device clear	All
00010101	PPU	Parallel poll uncon-figure	All
00011000	SPE	Serial poll enable	All
00011001	SPD	Serial poll disable	All
001aaaaa		Set device as listener	aaaaaa
00111111		Unlisten	All
010aaaaa		Set device as talker	aaaaaa
01011111		Untalk	All
011aaaaa		Secondary address	
01100000		Parallel poll enable	
01110000		Parallel poll disable	

Here address means that the address or addresses of the devices to be affected follow the command word. When setting listeners or a talker the lower 5 bits aaaaa represent the binary value of the device number. Note that a device number of 31 causes any listeners (unlisten) or talkers (untalk) to be disabled.

Secondary address commands are generally used as extra commands which may be decoded by a particular instrument to control dedicated operations within that instrument. Two of these commands are reserved since they are used to enable and disable parallel poll operation.

Handshake operation

Figure 75 shows the sequence of events during a data transfer across the bus.

When all active listeners are ready to accept data the NRFD line goes false and the talker places the data

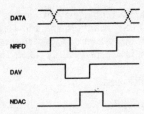

Figure 75 Timing of signals on IEEE488 instrument bus

signal on the bus. When the data is valid the DAV line is set true by the talker. At this point listeners will set their NRFD outputs true and then accept the data from the bus. After each listener has accepted the data it releases its NDAC line to the false state. When the talker detects NDAC false it resets its DAV line to false. When all listeners are ready to accept new data the NRFD line goes false and a new data transfer cycle can start.

10 Serial input and output

Although parallel I/O systems provide fast and simple data transfer they have the disadvantage of requiring complex multiwire cables. Whilst such cables are fine for connecting up, say, a printer which is located close to the computer they are not particularly suited for long distance communication, such as via a telephone or radio link.

An alternative approach to data transmission is to send the individual data bits one after another along a single wire. This technique is called serial transmission and most computers have facilities for handling this type of data transfer.

In serial output the data state for each bit is placed on the output line for a fixed time period and then each of the other bits is applied in turn during successive time periods until the entire word has been sent. This process is usually achieved by using a shift register which consists of a chain of flip-flops connected so that the output from one stage acts as the data input for the next. When a clock pulse is applied simultaneously to all of the flip-flops the data pattern stored in them moves along by one position along the chain. To produce a serial output the data word is first of all loaded in parallel into the set of flip-flops making up the shift register. By taking the output from the stage at the end of the chain each bit is placed on the output line in turn for a fixed time period.

At the receiving end a similar shift register is used to reassemble the data word. In this case the serial signal is applied to the input of the first stage in a shift register. The data word shifts into the register 1 bit at a time as clock pulses are applied. After the appropriate number of clock pulses have occurred the complete word is held in the data register and may then be read out in parallel.

In a serial transmission system the main problem is to ensure that the shift registers at each end of the link operate in synchronism and this could be achieved by sending the clock signal along a separate wire. To ensure accurate decoding at the receiving end it is usual to shift the phase of the clock signal so that the receiving shift register is clocked at about the middle of the bit period where the data level is stable. This avoids possible errors due to the edges of the bit pulses being rounded off or distorted by transmission along the line.

A further requirement is word synchronization which will indicate when the complete word is available in the receiving shift register. Again this could be achieved by sending a synchronization pulse along a further wire. In practical systems both the clock and word synchronization are achieved by adding extra signals to the serial data rather than sending signals on separate wires.

Asynchronous transmission

One synchronization scheme is the asynchronous mode of transmission in which the clock and word synchronization are carried out at the start of every serial data word. This technique was originally developed for use in automatic telegraph circuits where the rate at which operators would type individual symbols could vary.

In asynchronous mode it is assumed that the local decoding clock generated at the receiving end of the link is sufficiently stable in frequency to correctly decode all of the bits of a single data word. If we assume that the data word is 8 bits long and that the clock pulse on the last bit of the word must not deviate by more than, say, a quarter of a bit period from the centre of the eighth bit then the clock needs to maintain its frequency within 4% during the word time. This is relatively easy to achieve with simple logic clocks.

If the clock frequency is correct then all that needs to be done is to synchronize the clock at the beginning of each data word. This is done by adding a START bit at the beginning of the data stream. Between words the signal is held at the mark level. The START bit is always a space and on detection of this bit the decoding clock starts running. After the data word has been sent a further 1 or 2 bits at the mark level are included. These are the STOP bits and ensure that when words are transmitted one after another there will always be at least one mark bit before the START bit of the next data word. Since the START bit occurs at the beginning of every data word it also provides the required word synchronization signal. Figure 76 shows a typical asynchronous serial data word.

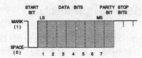

Figure 76 Signal format for one data word in an asynchronous serial data transmission

A disadvantage of the asynchronous serial system is that the START and STOP bits and any additional mark periods between successive data words do not convey any useful information. Thus, of perhaps eleven serial bits, there may only be seven that are carrying information. Thus some 30% of the transmission time is wasted.

Synchronous transmission

The alternative method of synchronization is to synchronize the clock and word start point at the beginning of a block of data and then just send successive words one after another with no further synchronization. The data coding is usually arranged so that at least one data transition will occur in each data word so that the clock timing and phase can be maintained in synchronism with the received signal. The receiver decoding clock is usually crystal controlled so that its timing will remain accurate throughout the received data block. In some systems a clock derived from the transmitter system may be sent along a separate line to provide the decoding clock.

The block of data sent is typically at least 256 bytes long. Now the redundant signal consists of perhaps two or three bytes for synchronization at the start of the data block and two or three words for error checking at the end of the block. With a 256 byte block some 98% of the transmitted signal is carrying information.

Synchronous transmission schemes come in two basic forms known as character-oriented protocols (COPs) or bit-oriented protocols (BOPs). In the character protocol the data is a sequence of 8-bit character codes. In a bit-oriented protocol the data consists of a stream of bits and individual data items within the stream may be any number of bits in length.

Character orientated protocols

The bisync protocol is an example of this type of synchronous transmission scheme. In bisync the initial clock synchronization is achieved by sending 1 or 2 bytes in which alternate bits are set at 0 and 1. Next a one or two byte synchronization word is sent to signal the start of the data frame. The data pattern in the synchronization word is usually chosen so that it is unique and when the receiver unit detects this pattern it will know the point at which the following data words and can start to decode the message.

Each block of transmitted data is called a frame and for the bisync mode a typical frame has the format shown in Figure 77. After the synchronization word there is an SOH (start of header) control character which marks the start of the header section. The header may contain source and destination addresses and perhaps a message serial number. The header section is followed by an STX (start text) control code which indicates the start of the message proper. The message itself may be either a string of ASCII character codes or a string of binary data bytes. After the message section comes an ETX (end text) or ETB (end transmission block) code to mark the end of the message. Finally there is a cyclic redundancy check (CRC) word which is used to detect errors in the received data. After the end of the block the signal may either go to the mark state or alternatively a series of synchronous idle (SYN) codes may be sent. This idle code is a stream of alternate 0 and 1-bits and may simply be used to keep the receiving and transmitting clocks in synchronism. The next transmission block starts again with a SYNC word.

SYNC	SOH	HEADER	STX	TEXT	ETB	CRC

Figure 77 Layout of a bisynchronous transmission frame

When binary data words are sent as a message a problem can occur with binary numbers that correspond to ASCII control codes such as SOH, ETX etc. To avoid misinterpretation of such codes a real control code is preceded by a DLE (data link escape) control code and is then recognized as a control code at the receiving end. A data byte is not preceded by

DLE and is treated as data.

Bit-orientated protocols

Bit-orientated protocols have the advantage that the data format in the block is flexible. In the bisync frame the layout of the data in the block was defined by inserting control codes into the data stream. In a BOP scheme an agreed data format for the frame must be used so that the receiving system knows how to sort out the individual sections of the control and message data.

Examples of bit orientated protocols are high level data link control (HDLC), advanced data communication control procedure (ADCCP) and synchronous data link control (SDLC). The block format for the widely used HDLC transmission protocol is shown in Figure 78.

| FLAG | HEADER | DATA | CRC | FLAG |

Figure 78 Layout of an HDLC transmission frame

At the start of the block is a synchronizing byte known as the opening flag which is usually 01111110. This is followed by an address field of one or more bytes which gives the source and destination addresses for the message. This is followed by a 1- or 2-byte control field which indicates the type of message being sent and also its frame sequence number. Following this there is an information field which contains the message itself and may be of any length but is often limited to 256 bytes. Finally there is a CRC byte and a closing flag byte which is the same as the opening flag.

In this type of transmission it is possible that a string of bits in the message section could have the same format as the opening or ending flag. If transmitted such a sequence could be interpreted as an end flag and part of the message would then be lost. To avoid this problem a technique known as bit stuffing is used. Whenever a string of six successive 1 bits is detected in the message stream an extra 0 bit is inserted between the fifth and sixth 1 bits to ensure that a false flag code is not sent. At the receiving end these extra bits are detected and stripped out of the data stream to restore the original message data.

Serial interface chips

Motorola 6850 ACIA

The 6850 asynchronous communications interface adapter (ACIA) chip provides a versatile asynchronous serial input–output interface and is particularly designed for use with the 6800 and 6500 series processors. This chip can also be used with the 16/32-bit 68000 series processors.

The chip contains four programmable registers. Two are used as data registers for transmit and receive operations and the others are a control register and a status register. Although there are four registers the ACIA occupies only two successive addresses in the CPU memory map. This is because the control and transmit registers are only selected during write operations whilst receive data and status are read only registers. A register select line determines whether a data or control/status register is selected. Three chip select lines provide some flexibility for address decoding.

Apart from the transmit and receive data registers the 6850 also contains transmit and receive buffer registers which hold the data currently being sent or received. Loading a word into the transmit register will automatically cause the word to be transferred to the transmit buffer if the latter is empty. If a word is currently being sent the data transfer to the buffer does not occur until the current data has been sent. In the same way the last word received is held in the data register whilst the next word is being received.

Figure 79 shows the pin connections of the 6850 ACIA.

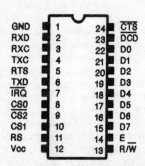

Figure 79 Pin connections for the 6850 ACIA

Signal functions

D0–D7	Data bus
RXC	Receive clock input
RXD	Receive data input
TXC	Transmit clock input
TXD	Transmit data output
IRQ	Interrupt request output
CS0–CS2	Chip select inputs
RS	Register select input
R/W	Read/write input
RTS	Request to send output
CTS	Clear to send input
DCD	Data carrier detect input
E	Enable

Power supply Vcc = +4.75 V to +5.25 V 60 mA

The RS line selects in conjunction with the R/W input the internal register that is to be accessed. RS = 0 selects the control or status register whilst RS = 1 selects the transmit or receive data register. Since control and transmit registers are write only they are selected by R/W = 0 (write) whilst the status and receive data registers are read only and are selected when R/W = 1 (read).

Control register

The control register bits act as follows:

Bits 0 and 1 Clock division or reset

B1	B0	Action
0	0	RXC and TXC used directly
0	1	RXC and TXC divided by 16
1	0	RXC and TXC divided by 64
1	1	Master reset

Note master reset must be programmed by software during initialization of the chip otherwise it will not function correctly.

Bits 2–4   Word format select

B4	B3	B2	Data bits	Stop bits	Parity
0	0	0	7	2	Even
0	0	1	7	2	Odd
0	1	0	7	1	Even
0	1	1	7	1	Odd
1	0	0	8	2	None
1	0	1	8	1	None
1	1	0	8	1	Even
1	1	1	8	1	Odd

Bits 5 and 6   Transmitter control

These bits govern the action of the RTS output and transmitter interrupt. A BREAK signal may also be generated.

B6	B5	RTS	Tx IRQ	Break
0	0	Low	Disabled	No
0	1	Low	Enabled	No
1	0	High	Disabled	No
1	1	Low	Disabled	Sent

During a BREAK transmission the serial data output is held at the 0 level.

Bit 7   Receiver interrupt

If $B7 = 1$ the receiver interrupt is enabled and when $B7 = 0$ the receive interrupt is disabled.

Status register

The bits in this register indicate various error and interrupt status.

Bit 0   Rx register full
Bit 1   Tx buffer empty
Bit 2   DCD state
Bit 3   CTS state
Bit 4   Frame error
Bit 5   Overrun error
Bit 6   Parity error
Bit 7   IRQ flag bit

Bit 1 is reset when a word is read from the Rx data register and bit 2 is reset by writing a word to the Tx data register. Bits 4, 5 and 6 are reset when data is read from the Rx register.

Motorola 6852 SSDA

The 6852 is a synchronous serial data adapter (SSDA) and is designed for use with 6800 series processors to provide a byte-orientated synchronous serial communications interface using a bisync type format.

The 6852 comes in a 24-pin dual in-line package whose connections are shown in Figure 80.

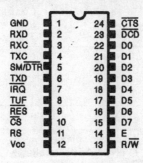

Figure 80 Pin connections for the 6852 SSDA

Signal functions

D0–D7	Data bud
CS	Chip select
RS	Register select
R/W	Read write input (write = 0)
E	System clock
RES	Reset (active low)
RDC	Receive clock input
RXD	Receive data input
TXC	Transmit clock input
TXD	Transmit data output
IRQ	Interrupt request out (active low)
SM/DTR	Sync match output/DTR input
TUF	Transmit underflow output
CTS	Clear to send input
DCD	Data carrier detect input

Power supply Vcc = +4.75 V to +5.75 V

Register selection

The 6852 contains seven programmable registers. Three are selected directly by the RS and R/W control lines. In the read mode the status register is read if RS = 0 and the RX data register is read when RS = 1. In write mode with RS = 0 control register 1 (CR1) is selected. With RS = 1 one of the remaining registers is selected according to the states of bits 6 and 7 of control register CR1.

Control 1		
Bit 7	Bit 6	Register selected
0	0	Control 2 (CR2)
0	1	Control 3 (CR3)
1	0	Sync word
1	1	Transmit data

Status register

Bit	Function
0	Rx data available
1	Tx data register available
2	Data carrier detect
3	Clear to send
4	Transmitter underflow
5	Receiver over-run
6	Receive parity error
7	Interrupt request

Control register CR1

Bit	Action
0	Receiver reset
1	Transmitter reset
2	Strip sync characters
3	Clear sync
4	Tx interrupt enable
5	Rx interrupt enable
6	Address 1
7	Address 2

Control register CR2

Bit	Function
0	SM/DTR output select (0 = DTR)
1	DTR output state or SM output enable
2	1 or 2 byte transfer (2 byte = 0)
3	Word length select
4	Word length select
5	Word length select
6	Transmit sync on underflow
7	Error interrupt enable

When SM is selected (bit 0 = 1) and bit 1 is at 0 a pulse is output at the SM/DTR pin when a synchronous code is detected. If bit 1 = 1 the output is held at 0.

Word length selection

B5	B4	B3	Word length
0	0	0	7-bits even parity
0	0	1	7-bits odd parity
0	1	0	7-bits no parity
0	1	1	8-bits no parity
1	0	0	8-bits even parity
1	0	1	8-bits odd parity
1	1	0	9-bits even parity
1	1	1	9-bits odd parity

Word length includes the parity bit.

Control register CR3

Bit	Function
0	Ext/int sync mode (ext = 1)
1	1 or 2 sync characters (1 sync = 1)
2	Clear CTS status bit
3	Clear TUF status bit
4	Not used
5	Not used
6	Not used
7	Not used

In external synchronous mode a transition to low can be applied to the DCD input to synchronize the receiver when the external synchronous circuit detects a synchronous code.

Intel 8251A PCI

The 8251A programmable communications interface (PCI) chip is primarily designed for use with the 8085 and 8086 processors but can fairly easily be interfaced with the Zilog Z80 CPU. The chip provides both asynchronous and synchronous serial input–output facilities which are fully programmable.

The 8251A has a 28-pin DIL package whose connections are shown in Figure 81.

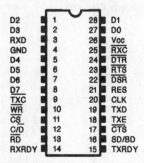

Figure 81 Pin connections for the 8251A PCI

Signal functions

D0–D7	Data bus (8 bit)
WR	Write control input
RD	Read control input
CS	Chip select input
CLK	Clock input (usually CPU clock)
RESET	Reset input
C/D	Control/data select input
RXC	Receive clock input
RXD	Receive data input
RXR	Receive data ready output
TXC	Transmit clock input
TXD	Transmit data output
TXE	Transmitter empty output
TXR	Transmitter ready output
RTS	Ready to send output
CTS	Clear to send input

DTR	Data terminal ready input
DSR	Data set ready input
SYND/BRKD	Sync/break detect (I/O)

Power Supply Vcc = +4.75 V to +5.25 V at 100 mA

RXC and TXC determine the baud rate for the serial receive and transmit.

In asynchronous mode the BRKD line is an output indicating that an all zero word has been received. In synchronous mode the SYND may be used as an output to indicate that the internal synchronous detector has detected a SYNC word or it may be programmed as an input when an external SYNC detection system is used.

The input C/D is used as a register select input. When it is at 0 either the Rx or Tx data register is selected according to the status of the RD and WR control lines. Rx operates with read operations and Tx is selected for write operations. When C/D is at 1 the status register is selected by read and the control register by write operations. If both RD and WR are at 1 the data bus lines of the chip are disabled.

Inside the 8251A there are effectively four control registers which need to be programmed. These are the mode register, two 8-bit registers for the SYNC word and the command register. The mode register is selected immediately after a reset action either by an input to the reset pin or by a command to the command register. Once data has been written to the mode register the other registers are automatically selected in sequence with the command register remaining active until another reset is performed. The SYNC word registers are only selected when the synchronous mode has been set in the mode register.

Mode register

Asynchronous/synchronous mode select (bits B0, B1)

B1	B0	Function
0	0	Synchronous mode
0	1	Asynchronous Rxc/Txc = baud rate
1	0	Asynchronous Rxc/Txc = 16 × baud rate
1	1	Asynchronous Rxc/Txc = 64 × baud rate

Character length (Bits B2, B3)

B3	B2	Character length
0	0	5-bits
0	1	6-bits
1	0	7-bits
1	1	8-bits

Parity mode (bits B4, B5)

B5	B4	Parity action
0	0	No parity
0	1	Odd parity
1	0	No parity
1	1	Even parity

STOP bit selection (B6, B7) (asynchronous mode)

B7	B6	No. of STOP bits
0	0	Not valid
0	1	1 STOP bit
1	0	1.5 STOP bits
1	1	2 STOP bits

When synchronous mode is selected bits 6 and 7 determine the operation of synchronous generation and detection.

SYNC detection (B6, B7) (synchronous mode)

B7	B6	SYND	No. of SYNC characters
0	0	Output	2
0	1	Input	2
1	0	Output	1
1	1	Input	1

When the SYND line is set as an input and the internal synchronous detector is disabled and an external synchronous code detector must be used to feed a pulse to the SYND input when a SYNC code is detected.

Command register

Bit	Action
0	Transmit enable (1) or disable (0)
1	When set at 1 makes the DTR output 0
2	Receive enable (1) or disable (0)
3	Normal (0) Send BRK (TXD = 0) (1)
4	0 = normal 1 = reset error flags FE, OE, PE
5	0 = normal 1 = set RTS to 0
6	0 = normal 1 = internal reset
7	0 = normal 1 = search for SYNC word

Status register

Bit	Function
0	Tx ready for new data
1	Rx data ready
2	Tx empty
3	Parity error detected
4	Overrun error detected
5	Framing error detected
6	SYNC word detected
7	Data set ready (DSR input = 0)

When the status condition occurs the corresponding status bit is set at 1.

Other serial interface chips

Some other types of serial interface chips available are:

6854	Advanced data link controller (sync)
Z80-SIO	Dual serial I/O (async and sync) for Z80
Z80-DART	Dual async serial I/O
8273	Sync serial I/O (HDLC/SDLC)

EIA RS232C serial link standard

The RS232C interface standard was devised by the American Electronics Industry Association (EIA) and defines the signal levels and connections for serial interfaces between the signal source and the transmission line or modem. The equivalent European standard is CCITT V24.

The standard connector used is the 25-pin D type although some equipment may use different connectors but retain the same same signal levels and names.

On the standard D connector the signals are:

Pin	Abbreviation	Signal	Direction DTE	DCE
1	FG	Frame ground		
2	TXD	Transmitted data	Out	In
3	RXD	Received data	In	Out
4	RTS	Request to send	Out	In
5	CTS	Clear to send	In	Out
6	DSR	Data set ready	In	Out
7	SG	Signal ground		
8	DCD	Data carrier detect	In	Out
9		Test signal		
10		Test signal		
11		Not used		
12	SDCD	Secondary DCD		
13	SCTS	Secondary CTS		
14	STXD	Secondary Txd		
15	TXC	Transmitter clock		
16	SRXD	Secondary Rxd		
17	RXC	Receiver clock		
18		Not used		
19	SRTS	Secondary RTS		
20	DTR	Data terminal ready	Out	In
21	SQ	Signal quality		
22	RI	Ring indicator	In	Out
23		Signal rate select		
24		External TXC		
25		Not used		

The three key signals are transmitted data (Txd), received data (Rxd) and ground. Most computer systems also make use of a series of control signals as well. The request to send (RTS) signal is used to tell the remote device to prepare to receive data. The

CTS (clear to send) signal is used to tell the remote unit that it can transmit data. A data terminal ready signal is used to indicate that the remote unit is ready to communicate. The data carrier detect (DCD) signal is mainly for use with modems and is used to indicate that the local modem is receiving a carrier tone from the remote unit.

In an RS232C system the computer is effectively the terminal and acts as the data terminal equipment (DTE). For long distance communication a modulator–demodulator (modem) unit would be used to couple the signals to say a phone line. This modem acts as the remote unit for the computer and acts as the data communications equipment (DCE). Peripheral units such as printers with a serial input would normally be considered as the DCE unit.

The RS232C system defines the signal levels on the line. Normally the line is designed to switch from a signal level of $+12$ V representing the space condition to a level of -12 V for the mark condition. Many systems actually run with signal swings from $+6$ V to -6 V. The minimum signal level is usually specified as $+3$ V to -3 V. Some computer equipment is designed to work with normal TTL level signals but devices outputting such signals may not operate correctly when feeding another unit with a standard RS232C input.

The main problem with sending a switched logic signal along a line is that the signal is both attenuated and distorted as it travels along the line. These effects are caused partly by the inductance and capacitance of the line itself and may also be influenced by other interfering signals that may be picked up by the line. Typical of such interfering signals might be power line hum from mains power cables running near the signal cable.

If the distortion and interfering signals become large enough they can cause errors in the received signal. In a typical system using say twisted pair cable for the line the transmission should be reliable up to distances of perhaps 30 to 50 metres but beyond this special precautions such as the use of special cables and improved line drivers and receivers are usually desirable.

EIA RS449 serial link standard

Because of the problems with the RS232C standard over long links a new standard known as EIA RS449 was developed to define the signal connections for an improved serial link. This system allows for the use of balanced transmission lines for all of the important signals. There are also associated standards RS422 and RS423 which define the signal levels and line arrangements to be used in an RS449 system.

The RS449 scheme uses a 37-way D type connector for the primary channel and an additional 9-way D type may be added to provide a secondary channel.

Primary channel 37-way

Pin	Signal	Function
1	SCRN	Screen
2	SI	Signal rate indicator
3		Not used
4	SD+	Send data (+)
5	ST+	Send timing (+)
6	RD+	Receive data (+)
7	RS+	Request to send (+)
8	RT+	Receive timing (+)
9	CS+	Clear to send (+)
10	LL	Local loop back
11	DM+	Data mode (+)
12	TR+	Terminal ready (+)
13	RR+	Receiver ready (+)
14	RL	Remote loopback
15	IC	Incoming call
16	SR	Signal rate select
17	TT+	Terminal timing (+)
18	TM	Test mode
19	SG	Signal ground
20	RC	Receive common
21		Not used
22	SD−	Send data (−)
23	ST−	Send timing (−)
24	RD−	Receive data (−)
25	RS−	Request to send (−)
26	RT−	Receive timing (−)
27	CS−	Clear to send (−)
28	IS	In service
29	DM−	Data mode (−)

30	TR $-$	Terminal ready ($-$)
31	RR $-$	Receive ready ($-$)
32	SS	Select standby
33	SQ	Signal quality
34	NS	New signal
35	TT $-$	Terminal timing ($-$)
36	SB	Standby indicator
37	SC	Send common

Secondary channel 9-pin

Pin	Signal	Function
1	SCRN	Screen ground
2	SRR	Secondary Rx ready
3	SSD	Secondary send data
4	SRD	Secondary receive data
5	SG	Signal ground
6	RC	Receive common
7	SRS	Secondary RTS
8	SCS	Secondary CTS
9	SC	Send common

EIA RS422A line signal standard

In this standard the signals on the $+$ and $-$ signal lines are complementary so that if the $+$ line goes to its high state the $-$ line will go to its low state. The normal signal levels are $+6$ V for one state and -6 V for the alternate state. Thus if a ($+$) wire is at $+6$ V the corresponding $-$ wire will be at -6 V. When the logic state changes the $+$ wire becomes -6 V and the $-$ wire $+6$ V. Thus there is always a 12 V difference between the two lines. The main advantage of this balanced line scheme is that common mode signals, relative to the common ground, cancel out thus reducing noise and interference problems.

The line driver circuit must be able to drive the line correctly when the line is terminated by a 450 Ω load and in the case of a short circuited line the driver must limit the line current to 150 mA. The line signal normally swings between $+6$ V and -6 V at the transmitter output and the receiver is usually designed to respond correctly provided the received signal swing is greater than $+1$ V to -1 V. The maximum data rate for a line length of 12m is about 10M bits per second. With a data rate of 100k bits per second line lengths of the order 1000 m are permissible.

EIA RS423A line signal standard

In the RS423A scheme each of the − signal lines is used as a separate signal return and the + line switches between +6 V and −6 V relative to its own − line. The line loading and current limit requirements for the driver are the same as for an RS422A system. The maximum bit rate for RS423A is about 100k bits per second at distances up to 100 m and 1000 bits per second for distances up to 1000 m.

Because the RS423A signals are single ended rather than differential this scheme is more or less compatible with RS232A drivers and receivers. One consideration is that signals from an RS232C device have a larger voltage swing and will need to be attenuated to bring them within the signal limits for the RS423A receiver.

Line drivers and receivers

Although discrete transistor line drivers and receivers could be used most systems use specialized line driver and receiver chips for these functions. For RS232C systems the commonly used devices are the 1488 quad line driver and 1489 quad line receiver. In the 1488 three of the drivers (2, 3 and 4) provide an AND function whilst the fourth is a simple driver amplifier. The line receiver devices each have a control input which may be used to adjust the threshold level at which the receiver responds and may also be used to provide filtering to reduce the effects of noise on the line.

Figure 82 shows the pin connections for the 1488 line driver and those of the 1489 receiver are shown in Figure 83.

For RS422A/RS423A systems the AM26L31 quad differential line driver and the AM26LS32 quad line receiver may be used.

The S5/8 serial interface

Recently, a simplified serial interface scheme has been devised for use with personal computer systems. This makes use of 8-pin DIN connectors for the serial link cable. The pin allocations are:

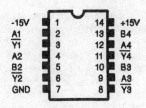

1488
LINE DRIVER

Figure 82 Pin connections for 1488 line driver

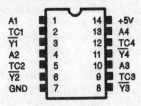

1489
LINE RECEIVER

Figure 83 Pin connections for 1489 line receiver

Pin	Signal	Function
1	DINP	Serial data input
2	GRND	Signal ground
3	DOUT	Serial data output
4	HINP	Handshake input
5	HOUT	Handshake output
6	SINP	Secondary data input
7	SOUT	Secondary data output
8	V+	+5 V supply (up to 20 mA)

Unlike RS232, there is no differentiation between senders and receivers or DCE and DTE devices. Data and handshake lines need to be crossed over in the link cable so that the data output of one device feeds the data input of the device at the other end of the line. This also applies to handshake signals.

Devices containing a 5 V power source are designated D type whilst those which do not contain a power supply are designated S type. In a typical system an S type device would derive its power from the D type device via the V + line of the link cable. Typically the computer would be a D type device whilst a unit such as a modem might be an S type.

The signal levels are based on a nominal 5 V logic swing and are similar to those produced by a typical TTL or CMOS logic circuit. For the line driver the high state is + 4.35 V minimum and the low state is + 0.15 V maximum. The driver should be short circuit protected and be capable of driving a capacitive load of at least 2.5 nF.

At the receiving end the input resistance should be 47k Ω and the threshold for a low signal should be + 0.9 V whilst the high signal threshold is + 3.85 V. The input should however be capable of handling signals of at least + 25 V to − 25 V without being damaged. This allows the possibility of feeding the S5/8 interface with signals generated to the RS232 standard.

The signal format is asynchronous with one START bit, eight data bits and one STOP bit. No bits are allocated for parity checking so error detection should be done by using a CRC word at the end of each transmission block. The standard data rate is 9600 baud.

The low (0.15 V) level is equivalent to the mark state in an RS232 system and the high (4.35 V) level represents the space state.

Modems

For long distance serial communication such as along public telephone lines, special techniques are used. The phone line is primarily designed to handle speech communications and is not particularly suited for carrying digital signals. The solution to this problem is to convert the mark and space signals into audio frequency tones. Each character of the serial signal will now consist of a sequence of tones instead of a simple digital signal.

At the transmitting end the digital signal is fed to a modulator unit which generates the appropriate tone signals. At the receiving end the tone signals are fed to demodulator unit which extracts the original serial logic signals. The modulator and demodulator are usually combined in a single unit called a modulator–demodulator (MODEM).

11 Counters and timers

Each major series of microprocessors has support chips which provide timing and counting facilities. Although in simple systems such operations could be provided by using conventional logic chips the advantage of the dedicated counter/timer devices is that they are designed to be programmed by the CPU to provide a wide range of counting and timing operations. Typical of such counter-timer chips are the Intel 8253 PIT, Motorola 6840 PTM and Zilog Z8430 CTC.

When used for simple time delay generation the counter is loaded with a count value and starts to count down. When the count value reaches zero a status register bit is set and an interrupt signal may also be generated. In some modes of operation an output pulse may also be produced from the counter output line. The length of the time delay is governed by the data value loaded into the counter when it is started.

Most types provide continuous counting modes which may be used for waveform generation. In the continuous count mode the preset starting value is held in a separate register and when the count reaches zero the count register is loaded again with the preset starting value and starts a new count cycle. The output line from the counter may be arranged either to change state or to produce a short pulse each time the count reaches zero. The result is either a square wave or a train of pulses and the frequency of the output waveform is determined by the preset starting value programmed into the counter.

Counters usually have an input gate line which allows the count action to be started or stopped. The clock for the counter may either be derived from the CPU clock or may be fed in to an external clock input. The counter can be used as a simple event counter by applying a pulse to its external clock input each time an event occurs. The counter is then set to zero and the gate input is activated to allow counting to start. After some preset time interval the gate is turned off to stop the count and the contents of the counter may be read. A point to remember here is that most of the counter timer devices are arranged so that the counter counts down rather than up.

For pulse period measurement the signal to be measured is applied to the gate line so that counting takes place only whilst the input is active. Some types also permit period measurement on an input waveform. In this case the counter starts counting on, say, the 0 to 1 transition of the input and stops counting on the next 0 to 1 transition.

Intel 8253 PIT

The 8253 is a programmable interval timer (PIT) which contains three independently programmable 16-bit binary counters. These counters may be operated to act either as delay timers or as event counters.

The pin connections of the 24-pin DIL package are shown in Figure 84.

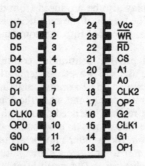

Figure 84 Pin connections for the 8253 PIT

Signal functions

D0–D7	8-bit data bus
CLKn	Clock input for counter n
GATEn	Gate input for counter n
OUTn	Output from counter n
RD	Read control input
WR	Write control input
CS	Chip select input
A0, A1	Address inputs

Power supply Vcc = +4.5 V to +5.5 V.

Register selection

The address inputs A0, A1 select the internal registers.

A1	A0	Action
0	0	Read or write counter 0
0	1	Read or write counter 1
1	0	Read or write counter 2
1	1	Write control register

The control register allows selection of the counting mode for each counter and also determines the way in which data is read from or written to the selected counter. Individual counters may be programmed differently since each has its own control logic which is set up via the control register. The bits in this register operate as follows:

Bit	7	6	5	4	3	2	1	0
	SC1	SC0	RL1	RL0	M2	M1	M0	BCD

Bit 0 selects BCD or binary counting (BCD = 1, Binary = 0)

Mode selection

Bits 1–3 select operating mode as follows:

B3	B2	B1	Mode selected	
0	0	0	Mode 0	Simple time delay
0	0	1	Mode 1	Programmable one shot
0	1	0	Mode 2	Rate generator
0	1	1	Mode 3	Square wave generator
1	0	0	Mode 4	Software triggered strobe
1	0	1	Mode 5	Hardware triggered strobe

In mode 0 the counter output goes low when the mode is set. After the counter has been loaded it counts down from its loaded value. When the count reaches 0 the output goes high and an interrupt is generated.

In mode 1 the output goes low and the counter starts to count down after a trigger pulse with a rising edge is applied at the GATE input. When the count reaches 0 the output goes high and counting stops until another trigger input is received.

In mode 2 counting is continuous and the output goes low for one clock period at every *n* clock periods where *n* is the count value loaded into the counter.

Mode 3 is similar to mode 2 with continuous counting but the output changes state after every *n* clock periods to produce a square wave output.

In Mode 4 the counter starts a count down after it has been loaded and when the count reaches 0 the output goes low for one clock period then returns to its high state. The effect is to produce a strobe pulse at a programmed time interval after the counter is loaded.

Mode 5 is similar to mode 4 but here the counter does not start until a pulse with a rising edge is applied at the GATE input.

Read/load action

This is determined by bits 4 and 5 if the control word as follows:

B5	B4	Action
0	0	Counter latched
0	1	Read or load MSB only
1	0	Read or load LSB only
1	1	Read or load LSB then MSB

Bits 6 and 7 of the control word determine which counter is to be acted upon.

B7	B6	Selected counter
0	0	Counter 0
0	1	Counter 1
1	0	Counter 2
1	1	Illegal

In modes 0, 2, 3 and 4 the GATE input can be used to inhibit counting by setting it low and counting resumes when the GATE input goes high.

Motorola 6840 PTM

The 6840 programmable timer module (PTM) contains three independent 16-bit counters which may be programmed to operate in a variety of modes. It is designed to be interfaced directly to processors of the 6800 and 6500 series and is also compatible with the 68000 series 16-bit processors.

The pin connections of the 40 pin DIL package are as shown in Figure 85.

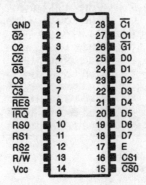

Figure 85 Pin connections for the 6840 PTM

Signal functions

D0–D7	Data bus
C1–C3	Clock inputs for counters 1–3
G1–G3	Gate inputs for counters 1–3
O1–O3	Outputs for counters 1–3
CS0, CS1	Chip select inputs
RS0–RS2	Register select inputs
R/W	Read/write control input
IRQ	Interrupt request output
Reset	Reset input
E	Enable input

The gate, clock, reset and CS0 inputs are all active low.

Register selection

The RS0, RS1 and RS2 inputs select the internal registers as follows:

RS2	RS1	RS0	R/W	Register
0	0	0	0	Write control 1 (CR2-bit 0 = 0)
0	0	0	0	Write control 3 (CR2-bit 0 = 1)
0	0	1	0	Write control 2

0	1	0	0	Write MSB buffer
0	1	1	0	Write counter 1 latches
1	0	0	0	Write MSB buffer
1	0	1	0	Write counter 2 latches
1	1	0	0	Write MSB buffer
1	1	1	0	Write counter 3 latches
0	0	0	1	Not used
0	0	1	1	Read status
0	1	0	1	Read counter 1
0	1	1	1	Read LSB buffer
1	0	0	1	Read counter 2
1	0	1	1	Read LSB buffer
1	1	0	1	Read counter 3
1	1	1	1	Read LSB buffer

Control registers

Bit 0 has a different function in each of the three control registers.

In CR1-bit 0 allows the timers to run (0) or holds them reset (1). In CR2-bit 0 selects either control 1 (0) or control 3 (1) and in CR3-bit 0 selects timer 3 prescaling (0 = none) (1 = t/8).

Bit 1 selects clock source 0 = external, 1 = E clock, bit 2 selects 16/8-bit mode 0 = 16-bit, 1 = dual 8-bit and bits 3, 4, 5 select counter mode.

B5	B4	B3	Mode
0	0	0	Continuous mode 1
0	0	1	Frequency comparison mode 1
0	1	0	Continuous mode 2
0	1	1	Pulse width mode
1	0	0	Single shot mode 1
1	0	1	Frequency comparison mode 2
1	1	0	Single shot mode 2
1	1	1	Pulse width mode 2

Bit 6 enables the IRQ output when it is set at 1 and bit 7 enables the output when it is set at 1.

Status register

Bit	Function
0	Timer 1 flag

1	Timer 2 flag
2	Timer 3 flag
7	Interrupt flag

If any timer times out it will set its own status flag bit and also the interrupt flag bit 7. Reading the status register followed by a read of the counter register will reset the counter flag. Alternatively, writing to a counter will reset the flag.

12 Multifunction chips

Several more complex support chips have been produced which can provide parallel and serial input–output and one or more counter-timers in a single chip.

6522 versatile interface adapter (VIA)

This interface chip designed for use with the 6500 series processors provides two parallel input–output ports, two timers and a serial shift register. Both timers use 16-bit counters and one can be used as an event counter. The serial shift register can be used to provide a simple serial input–output facility. The parallel ports provide similar facilities to those of the 6821.

The pin connections for the 40-pin dual in line package are shown in Figure 86.

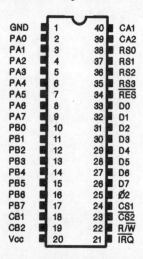

GND	1	40	CA1
PA0	2	39	CA2
PA1	3	38	RS0
PA2	4	37	RS1
PA3	5	36	RS2
PA4	6	35	RS3
PA5	7	34	$\overline{\text{RES}}$
PA6	8	33	D0
PA7	9	32	D1
PB0	10	31	D2
PB1	11	30	D3
PB2	12	29	D4
PB3	13	28	D5
PB4	14	27	D6
PB5	15	26	D7
PB6	16	25	Ø2
PB7	17	24	CS1
CB1	18	23	$\overline{\text{CS2}}$
CB2	19	22	R/$\overline{\text{W}}$
Vcc	20	21	$\overline{\text{IRQ}}$

Figure 86 Pin connections for the 6522 VIA

Signal functions

PA0–PA7	Port A I/O lines
PB0–PB7	Port B I/O lines
CA1, CA2	Port A handshake lines

CB1, CB2	Port B handshake lines
RS0–RS3	Register address inputs
RES	Reset input
D0–D7	Data bus
o2	Phase 2 clock from the CPU
CS1, CS2	Chip select inputs
IRQ	Interrupt request output

Power supply Vcc = +4.75 V to +5.25 V

The chip contains a total of sixteen registers which provide the input–output ports, timers, shift register, three control registers and a status register. These are selected by the register select inputs RS0–RS3.

Register addressing

RS3	RS2	RS1	RS0	Register
0	0	0	0	Port B data
0	0	0	1	Port A data (with handshake)
0	0	1	0	Data direction Register B
0	0	1	1	Data direction Register A
0	1	0	0	Timer 1 latch LSB
0	1	0	1	Timer 1 latch MSB
0	1	1	0	Timer 1 counter LSB
0	1	1	1	Timer 1 counter MSB
1	0	0	0	Timer 2 LSB and latch
1	0	0	1	Timer 2 MSB
1	0	1	0	Serial shift register
1	0	1	1	Auxiliary control register (ACR)
1	1	0	0	Peripheral control register (PCR)
1	1	0	1	Interrupt flag register (IFR)
1	1	1	0	Interrupt enable register (IER)
1	1	1	1	Port A data (no handshake)

The port A data register is duplicated at addresses 1 and 15. The difference is that reading or writing register 15 does not reset the handshake lines.

Data direction registers

Each bit in these registers corresponds to a data line on the port and if the bit is set at 1 the line becomes an output. After reset all bits are set at 0 so that all port lines are inputs. If the timers are used lines PB6 and PB7 are automatically used as input and output respectively irrespective of the setting of the data direction register.

Interrupt flag register (IFR)

Bit	Interrupt reported
0	CA2 input transition
1	CA1 input transition
2	Shift register has made 8 shifts
3	CB2 input transition
4	CB1 input transition
5	Timer 2 timed out
6	Timer 1 timed out
7	Interrupt request

Interrupt enable register (IER)

Bit	Action
0	Enable CA2 interrupt
1	Enable CA1 interrupt
2	Enable shift register interrupt
3	Enable CB2 interrupt
4	Enable CB1 interrupt
5	Enable Timer 2 interrupt
6	Enable Timer 1 interrupt
7	Enable/disable control

To enable an interrupt bit 7 and the appropriate interrupt bit are set at 1. To disable an interrupt, bit 7 is set at 0 and the desired interrupt bit is set at 1.

Auxiliary control register (AUX)

Bit	Action
0	Port A input enable
1	Port B input enable
2	Shift register control
3	Shift register control
4	Shift register control
5	Timer 2 mode one shot (0), event count (1)
6	Timer 1 output enable to PB7
7	Timer 1 mode, one shot (0), free run (1)

Before using port A or port B the appropriate input enable bits should be set in the auxiliary control register.

The shift register control bits act as follows:

B4	B3	B2	Action
0	0	0	Shift register disabled
0	0	1	Shift in (timer 2 as clock)
0	1	0	Shift in (02 as clock)
0	1	1	Shift in (CB1 as clock)
1	0	0	Free run shift (timer 2 clock)
1	0	1	Shift out (timer 2 clock)
1	1	0	Shift out (CPU clock)
1	1	1	Shift out (CB1 as clock)

The shift register uses the CB2 line for its data input when being used in the shift in mode. When the register is set up for the shift out mode the state of bit 7 is output on the CB2 line. In the free run mode the data is rotated continuously through the shift register and the state of bit 7 is output at CB2. The shift register can produce an interrupt after every eight shift operations. The shift register clock may be either the CPU clock, the time out of timer 2 or an external clock applied to CB1.

Timers 1 and 2 are normally clocked by the CPU clock (02). When timer 2 is operated as an event counter it is clocked by high/low transitions input to Port B line PB6.

Peripheral control register (PCR)

This controls the operation of the handshake lines for the parallel ports PA and PB. Bit 0 determines the active transition for input CA1 (1 = low/high). Similarly, bit 4 selects the active transition for CB1. Bits 1–3 control the action of CA2 whilst bits 5–7 control the action of CB2.

B3	B2	B1	In/Out	Action
0	0	0	Input	Interrupt on high/low (cleared by data read/write)
0	0	1	Input	Interrupt on high/low (cleared by IFR read/write)

0	1	0	Input	Interrupt on low/high (cleared by data read/write)
0	1	1	Input	Interrupt on low/high (cleared by IFR read/write)
1	0	0	Output	Set on CA1 active input reset on data read/write
1	0	1	Output	Low for one cycle after data register read/write
1	1	0	Output	Reset to low
1	1	1	Output	Set to high

68901 Multifunction peripheral (MFP)

This device is designed for use with the 68000 series of processors and provides two programmable parallel ports, four timers and a serial interface port. It also contains an interrupt priority handler. The connections to the 48-pin DIL package are shown in Figure 87.

Figure 87 Pin connections for the 68901 MFP

Signal lines

D0–D7	Data bus bidirectional
CS	Chip select
DS	Data strobe
DTACK	Data transfer acknowledge
RS1–RS5	Register select
RESET	Reset input
IRQ	Interrupt request output
IACK	Interrupt acknowledge
IEI	Interrupt enable input
IEO	Interrupt enable output
I/O 0–7	Input-output port lines
X1, X2	Timer clock crystal
TAI	Timer A input
TBI	Timer B input
TAO	Timer A output
TBO	Timer B output
TCO	Timer C output
TDO	Timer D output
SI	Serial input
SO	Serial output
RC	Receiver clock
TC	Transmitter clock
RR	Receiver ready
TR	Transmitter ready
Vcc	+5 V supply
GND	Ground

Internal registers

R0	I/O port data
R1	I/O port active edge
R2	I/O data direction
R3	Interrupt enable A
R4	Interrupt enable B
R5	Interrupt pending A
R6	Interrupt pending B
R7	Interrupt in service A
R8	Interrupt in service B
R9	Interrupt mask A
R10	Interrupt mask B
R11	Interrupt vector
R12	Timer A control
R13	Timer B control
R14	Timer C/D control
R15	Timer A data

R16 Timer B data
R17 Timer C data
R18 Timer D data
R19 Synchronous character
R20 USART control
R21 Receive status
R22 Transmit status
R23 USART data

In registers R3–R10 the bits are allocated as follows:

Group A registers (R3, R5, R7, R9)

Bit	Function
0	Timer B
1	Transmit error
2	Transmit buffer empty
3	Receive error
4	Receive buffer full
5	Timer A
6	I/O port bit 6
7	I/O port bit 7

Group B registers (R4, R6, R8, R10)

Bit	Interrupt
0	I/O port bit 0
1	I/O port bit 1
2	I/O port bit 2
3	I/O port bit 3
4	Timer D
5	Timer C
6	I/O port bit 4
7	I/O port bit 5

In each group the highest interrupt priority is allocated to bit 7 and the lowest to bit 0. The group A interrupts have a higher priority than those in group B.

When an interrupt occurs on an enabled channel (bit in R3, R4 set) the corresponding bit in registers R5, R6 is set. When the IRQ is acknowledged by the CPU the bit in the in service register (R7, R8) is set.

If the bit for the channel is set in the mask register then no IRQ is output to the CPU but the interrupt is recorded in the pending register R5, R6.

The vector register is used to provide an interrupt vector address to the CPU when an interrupt is acknowledged.

Timers A and B can operate in one of three modes. In delay mode the timer provides a continuous countdown action. When the count reaches 1 the output changes state and the counter is set to the value in its data register then continues to count. In event count mode external pulses applied to the timer input can be counted. The third mode is period measurement in which the counter is started by a pulse on its input and stopped by the next input pulse.

Timers C and D provide only the delay mode of operation.

All timers have an input prescaler which divides the input clock before applying it to the counter. The division ratios available are 4, 10, 16, 50, 64, 100 and 200.

An all zero control input stops the counter. In timers A and B a control register input value of 8 selects the event mode. Values above 8 select the period measurement mode and those below 8 the delay mode.

Register 20 controls the operation of the USART for serial I/O.

Bit 0 is not used. Bits 1 and 2 determine the parity operation as follows:

Bit 2	Bit 1	Parity mode
0	0	No parity
0	1	No parity
1	0	Odd parity
1	1	Even parity

Bits 3 and 4 select the format as follows:

Bit 4	Bit 3	Format
0	0	Synchronous
0	1	Asynchronous with 1 stop bit
1	0	Asynchronous with 1.5 stop bits
1	1	Asynchronous with 2 stop bits

Bits 5 and 6 select word length as follows:

Bit 6	Bit 5	Word length
0	0	8 bits
0	1	7 bits
1	0	6 bits
1	1	5 bits

Bit 7 selects the clock division ratio.
Bit 7 = 0   Clock not divided
Bit 7 = 1   Clock divided by 16

Receive status register

Bit	Function
0	Receiver enable
1	Synchronous strip enable
2	Match/character in progress
3	SYN/break detected
4	Frame error
5	Parity error
6	Overrun error
7	Buffer full

Transmit status register

Bit	Function
0	Transmit enable
1	High/low bit
2	High/low bit
3	Send break (async only)
4	End of transmission
5	Auto turnaround
6	Underrun error
7	Buffer empty

13 Analogue input and output

In the real world outside the microprocessor system most of the signals are likely to be analogue in form rather than digital. In an analogue signal the voltage, or current, level is proportional to the variable it represents. The computer, however, uses digital data signals which are either on or off. In order to interface the computer to real world signals an analogue to digital converter (ADC) is needed at the computer inputs and a digital to analogue converter (DAC) is needed at the computer outputs.

Digital to analogue converters

The usual form of digital to analogue converter uses a resistor network and electronic switches to generate weighted levels of voltage or current. The least significant bit of the data word will generate one unit of voltage when it is set at the 1 level and nothing when it is at the 0 level. The next higher bit produces two units, the third bit four units and so on. When added together the contributions from the bits in the word will produce an output voltage which is proportional to the numerical value of the word. This combined signal is then amplified to produce the desired output signal. A practical digital to analogue converter (DAC) uses a resistor ladder network arrangement as shown in Figure 88, where the switches S0 to S2 are solid state switches activated by bits 0 to 2 of the digital input word.

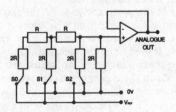

Figure 88 Basic circuit of a D/A converter

Typical DAC devices are built in a single integrated circuit and have an 8-bit digital input which provides an analogue output with 256 possible levels. The internal resistor network and switches may be arranged to output a signal which is always positive (unipolar) or one which can go both positive and negative (offset binary). It is also possible to arrange that the digital input is in BCD format with values from 0 to 99 giving 100 steps in the output signal level. More complex devices are available with 12- or 16-bit digital inputs giving a much finer resolution in the output analogue signal.

The resolution of a DAC is governed by the number of bits in the digital input it can handle. The speed of conversion is governed by the settling time which is the time between setting a new digital input and obtaining a stable analogue output.

Analogue to digital converters

For analogue to digital conversion a number of different techniques may be used. These various types of converters have advantages and disadvantages which make them more suited to some applications than others.

Single ramp integrating ADC

The simplest type of converter is the single ramp integrating type. This makes use of the fact that if a capacitor is charged with a constant current the voltage across the capacitor rises linearly with time. This type of conversion is sometimes used for joystick input signals on computers, such as the Apple II, where the conversion need not be particularly accurate.

In such a system the joystick contains a variable resistance which controls the charging current to a capacitor in the computer unit. At the start of each conversion cycle the capacitor is short-circuited to discharge it and when the short circuit is removed a counter is started. The counter is driven by a constant frequency clock and so measures the time interval. When the capacitor voltage reaches a preset voltage level the counter is stopped and the value in the counter will now be proportional to the position of the joystick control.

To measure an input voltage the capacitor may be

charged from a constant current source and the voltage across the capacitor is then compared with the input voltage being measured. When the capacitor starts to charge a timing counter is started. When the capacitor and input voltages are equal the counter is stopped and the value of the count is then proportional to the input voltage.

Dual ramp integrating ADC

The single ramp converter has the disadvantage that its accuracy depends upon the capacitor value, the timing clock frequency and the accuracy of the charging current to the capacitor. To overcome these problems a dual ramp converter is normally used.

In a dual ramp converter the capacitor is initially charged for a fixed time period using the input signal to provide the constant current charge. The time period is governed by the counter and is the time for one complete cycle through the counter range. At the end of the charging period the capacitor is switched to discharge at a fixed rate determined by a reference voltage and the counter starts counting again from zero. When the capacitor voltage reaches zero the count is read out and will be proportional to the input voltage applied. This type of converter has the advantage that errors due to capacitor value or timing clock variations are cancelled out giving a more accurate result.

The disadvantage of this type of converter is that it is relatively slow giving perhaps 10 readings per second. Its advantage is that because an integration technique is used the converter is relatively insensitive to noise and can also reject some types of interference such as mains hum. Digital multimeters normally use the dual ramp conversion technique.

DAC feedback converter

A variation on the signal ramp scheme is to run a counter from a fixed timing clock and feed the outputs of the counter to a DAC which then produces an output proportional to the count. The DAC output is then compared with the input signal and when the two are equal the counter is stopped and the counter value is used to provide the desired digital output.

Tracking converters

This is a variation of the counter and DAC feedback type of converter. In this system the counter counts up if the input signal is higher than the DAC output and it counts down if the input is lower. The result is that the count value follows or tracks the value of the input signal. Where input signal variations are relatively slow this type of converter gives virtually immediate output since the counter only has to make one or two steps to produce the correct output. When a large change in the input signal occurs there will be a delay before the counter catches up to produce the correct output.

Successive approximation converter

In the successive approximation converter a DAC feedback scheme similar to that in the counter feedback type is used but the counter is replaced by a register and some control logic.

At the start of the conversion cycle the register is cleared and then the MSB is set at 1 and the output of the DAC is compared with the input signal. If the input is lower than the DAC signal the register bit is reset to 0. The control logic then goes on to set the next lower bit of the register and a further comparison of DAC and input signals is made. The lower order bits are then set or reset in sequence until all bits have been adjusted when the DAC output should be approximately the same as the analogue input. At this point the data in the register will be the digital equivalent of the analogue input. This type of converter is fast in operation since for, say, a 10-bit converter only 10 test comparisons have to be made. A typical 10- or 12-bit converter running with a 1 MHz clock will carry out a conversion in some 12 to 15 microseconds compared with a conversion time of some 1 to 4 milliseconds for a counter or integration type converter.

Flash converters

For conversion of very high speed signals such as video waveforms a flash converter is generally used. This, in fact, consists of a vast array of signal comparators operating in parallel from the input signal. Each comparator checks one of the possible

discrete levels of the analogue signal which correspond to the steps in the digital output. The outputs
of the comparators are fed to a priority decoder
which selects the highest activated comparator and
sets up the corresponding digital bit pattern in the
output register. Such a converter may carry out an
analogue to digital conversion in a few nanoseconds
and can handle input frequencies up to several
megahertz.

The types of converter commonly designed for use
with microprocessors are usually of the dual ramp
integrating or successive approximation type. Those
designed for use with microprocessors usually have an
output latch register and also provide a signal to
indicate that conversion is complete. In many cases
the outputs will be tristate stages designed to interface
directly to a microprocessor data bus. Some
converters will also require a strobe input to initiate
a conversion cycle.

14 Display systems

For conventional indicator lamps and simple digital readouts a parallel output port is used to provide the control signals. Transistor buffers may be needed to handle the required output current and voltage for driving the displays. In the case of seven-segment digital indicators a binary to seven segment decoder using either TTL or CMOS chips will be required.

Most computer systems use a television type display to present output data. This builds up the picture on a cathode-ray tube screen by tracing a series of horizontal scan lines one after another down the screen to scan out the entire screen area. The image is built up by varying the intensity of the spot on the screen as each line is scanned. The European television standard picture is made up from 625 scan lines and is scanned 25 times a second.

A number of lines are left blank at the top and bottom of the display to allow time for the scan circuits to return from the bottom of the picture to the top ready for a new scan. To reduce the effects of flicker two scans down the screen are used to trace a complete picture. On the first scan all the odd numbered lines are traced out and on the second the even numbered lines are drawn. This technique is called interlaced scanning and each sweep down the screen is called a field. Thus each field consists of 312.5 lines of which 278 are actually used for the picture display. Most computer display circuits do not generate true interlaced scanning signals and thus display a picture which effectively has 278 lines traced out 50 times a second.

In America and Japan a different television standard is used. In this case the total number of lines for the picture is 512 and there are 30 complete pictures per second. Interlaced scanning is used for television pictures but for computer displays the effective picture is 222 lines high and repeated 60 times a second.

Text displays

Most early microcomputers provided a text only display on the screen. A text character is produced on the screen by selectively lighting dots in a small area of the screen as shown in Figure 89. In a typical system the character space might be eight dots wide by eight dots high. To give improved character shapes some systems use a dot matrix which is eight dots wide by sixteen dots high. For the text display the screen is divided up into an array of fixed character spaces. Typical screen formats are twenty-four rows of text with forty symbols displayed across each row and twenty-four rows with eighty symbols in each row.

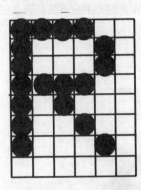

Figure 89   Use of a dot matrix to display a symbol

In a simple text display system the pattern of dots making up the character shapes are held in a read-only memory device which is generally referred to as a character generator ROM. This chip might contain the dot patterns for a set of perhaps 128 or 256 letters, figures and other symbols. It is usually arranged so that part of the ROM address represents the ASCII symbol code for the character to be displayed. The rest of the ROM address selects the row of dots being read out. The ROM usually outputs a complete horizontal row of dots at a time.

The basic text display system has the form shown in Figure 90. The character codes for the page of text to be displayed are held in a screen display RAM whose addressing is provided by the control logic. Character codes from the RAM are presented to the character generator ROM to call up the required dot patterns. Each row of dot data from the ROM is transferred in parallel into a shift register and then shifted out one bit at a time to provide the video signal which produces the dot pattern on the display screen. The addressing for the ROM and RAM is governed by control circuits so that as a line is traced on the screen one row of dots from the matrix for each symbol in the row of text is traced out by selecting the symbol in sequence from the RAM. For the next scan line the same set of characters is selected but the next lower row of dots is selected from the ROM. When all of the rows of dots in the row of text have been output a new set of text data for the next row of text is applied to the ROM. This process is repeated until the complete screen has been scanned and the entire scan is repeated fifty times a second.

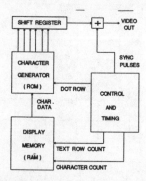

Figure 90 Block diagram of a text display system

The set of character codes for the page of text to be displayed is held in a RAM which is normally addressed by the display control logic. When new characters are to be written to the screen the addressing is temporarily switched to the CPU bus so that new data words can be written to the display RAM. In many computer systems the display RAM is actually part of the main computer memory and is addressed by the display control logic when the CPU is not accessing the bus system.

Graphics displays

Most modern microcomputers can display graphics images as well as text on the screen. In early computers this was achieved by using a conventional text display with a special ROM which included a series of graphics symbols such as lines, curves etc. These special symbols could then be placed in appropriate positions to produce limited graphics displays.

A variant of the text based graphics schemes is the 'mosaic' graphics scheme in which each text symbol space is divided into, say, four small blocks as shown in Figure 91. Now a set of additional text symbols is produced which defines all of the sixteen possible combinations of light and dark blocks in a symbol space. By combining these patterns of dots a crude graphics picture can be produced. Using a 40×24 symbol layout on the screen and four blocks in each symbol space a graphics resolution of eighty by forty-eight can be produced. Some systems divide the symbol space into six or eight blocks to give higher graphics resolution.

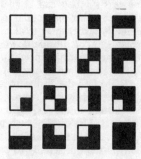

Figure 91 Symbols used for mosaic graphics

High resolution graphics

The text display screen is effectively built up from a vast array of individual picture elements or pixels. For a typical text display using a matrix of 8×8 dots per character with forty characters across the screen and twenty-five rows the screen is composed of an array of 320 by 200 pixels. If each of these pixels could be set individually then a high resolution graphics display can be produced. Higher resolution graphics displays giving 640×256, 640×400 are available on home computers and 1024×1024 or higher are common in dedicated graphics work-stations used for computer aided design.

In a system giving monochrome graphics each pixel can be either on or off. If one data bit is allocated to each pixel then each byte of the screen memory can hold the states of eight successive pixels along a display line. When the bit is at 1 the pixel is lit and a bit set at 0 indicates a black pixel. For a 640×400 resolution display each line of pixels requires 80 bytes of memory and the entire screen uses up 32,000 bytes of memory. Since each pixel on the screen is directly linked to a specific bit in the screen memory this type of graphics system is usually referred to as a 'bit mapped' graphics display.

Computers using a high resolution bit mapped graphics display usually produce text displays by simply copying the text symbol patterns on to the graphics screen. In most cases this is done by copying the bit pattern for a symbol from a character generator ROM into the appropriate positions in the graphics screen memory. One advantage of this approach is that text symbols can be placed at any position on the screen rather than in the fixed symbol positions of a simple text display system. It is also possible to display symbols upside down or turned through an angle to the normal upright position by merely altering the way in which the dot pattern is copied from the ROM into the display memory. New symbols are readily produced by simply generating the required dot pattern in the display memory.

To generate the graphics display each byte of the screen memory is loaded in turn into the video shift register and then shifted out serially to produce the video signal. In some systems the actual layout of the pixel bytes in the screen memory may be arranged to make the display of text simpler but this makes the calculation of the pixel memory address more complex when graphics figures are being drawn.

Computers with bit mapped graphics normally have a set of program routines available which allow lines and shapes to be drawn easily and for specified areas of the screen to be filled with white or black dots.

Colour displays

In a colour system the television display tube has three separate electron guns for red, green and blue signals respectively. On the screen there is a pattern of vertical stripes arranged in adjacent sets of three which produce red, green and blue light respectively. Each gun is arranged so that it only lights up the stripes for its own colour. One pixel position on the display covers a set of adjacent red, green and blue dots on the screen. At the normal viewing distance the eye combines the colours of these dots to produce a wide range of perceived colours.

By setting the red, green and blue dots either on or off a total of eight different colours can be produced on the screen. These are black, red (R), green (G), blue (B), yellow (R + G), magenta (R + B), cyan (B + G) and white (R + G + .B).

Colour attributes

For a text display in colour the video display system needs to know which colour each text symbol should have. The simplest scheme is to have a second area of memory which keeps a record of the colour for each symbol on the screen. This colour information is generally referred to as the colour attribute for the displayed symbol. Now the text screen memory holds the ASCII code for the symbol and the attribute memory holds a 3-bit code to indicate the combination of R, G and B to give the desired symbol colour. In the video display system three separate shift registers are used for the R, G and B signals. The colour attribute data is then used to gate the shift register outputs so that the appropriate combination of R, G and B dots is generated.

To handle colour in a high resolution graphics mode 2 or more bits are allocated to each pixel in the screen memory and these bits determine the colour for that pixel. If two bits are used for each pixel it can have one of four possible colours. In a simple system these might be black, red, green and white. The penalty when using a four-colour graphics system is that either the screen memory has to be twice as big or the picture resolution is reduced to half that of the monochrome version. Most modern computers have a colour mode which allows sixteen colours and uses 4-bits for each screen pixel. The usual scheme is to have the eight basic colours produced by combinations of R, G and B using three of the pixel data bits and the fourth bit may be used to provide a flashing pixel.

Colour palette systems

Some 16-bit computers use a colour palette system to select the colours of pixels displayed on their graphics screens. Here each displayable colour is defined by using say one of eight levels of red combined with one of eight levels each of green and blue. This gives a total of $8 \times 8 \times 8$ or 512 possible colours which can be selected. More advanced systems use 16 levels of red, green and blue to give a possible 4096 different colours.

To define each colour in a 512 colour system a 9-bit word is used with three bits each for the R, G and B components. To display the colour the three R bits are fed to a digital to analogue converter which produces one of eight output levels for the red signal. Similar converters are used to generate the green and blue video signals.

If the full range of colours were to be displayed simultaneously then 9 or 12 bits would be needed to define each pixel and the display memory would become enormous. To avoid this most systems allow a set of perhaps sixteen colours to be displayed at a time but each can be selected from the 512 or 4096 colours available. To define the sixteen colours each pixel is now represented by 4 data bits. In effect there are now four complete memory maps of the pixels on the screen and these are often referred to as memory planes.

The translation between the display colour number (0 to 15) and the actual colour code which is fed to the RGB output converters is done by allocating a set of sixteen words in the memory as palette registers. Each palette register contains the 9- or 12-bit code that defines the combination of R, G and B for one of the sixteen displayable colours. The 4-bit code held in the display memory for each pixel is used to select one of the palette registers and the output of that register is then fed to the R, G and B converters to produce the required video signal.

An Atari ST uses 3 bits each for R, G and B levels and has sixteen palette registers so that any sixteen of the 512 possible colours can be displayed on screen at a time. The Commodore Amiga provides thirty-two colours selected from a palette of 4096 colours. The more advanced IBM compatible PC machines using the VGA colour mode can provide 256 colours on screen at the same time.

Light pens

A light pen basically consists of a small photocell mounted in the tip of a pointer device which can be positioned so that the cell is close to the surface of the display screen. As the display scan sweeps across the screen under the tip of the light pen the photocell produces a pulse if the screen is lit at that point. By reading the display controller address counters when the light pen pulse occurs the position of the light pen on the screen display can be determined. Thus the light pen can be used to select points on the screen and with suitable software can control the graphics display to allow lines to be drawn or items displayed on the screen to be selected.

Display controllers

The logic required for generating a video display whether it be text or graphics is quite complex. Although some early computers used discrete logic chips for this purpose most computers today use dedicated controller chips to generate the timing and address signals for the video display. The screen memory is generally part of the main computer memory and some form of direct memory access scheme is used to allow the display controller to read data from the screen memory. Many personal computers use custom designed display controllers especially where palette type colour graphics systems are involved. Some computers use standard display controller chips such as the Motorola 6845 to provide the display timing and control signals.

6845 CRT controller (CRTC)

This chip is designed to replace most of the control logic needed to produce a text or graphics video display. It contains pixel and row counters and also generates the required memory address signals for accessing the video RAM and a character generator ROM. Pin connections are shown in Figure 92.

Internal registers allow the 6845 to be programmed to produce a wide range of display formats and it will generate the appropriate horizontal and vertical synchronization signals which when added to the pixel brightness signal will produce the desired composite video output signal.

Signal lines
MA0 MA13   Memory address (O)
D0 D7   Data bus (I/O)
RA0 RA4   Raster address (O)

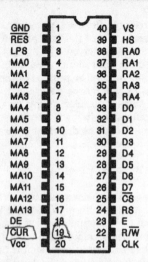

Figure 92 Pin connections for the 6845 CRTC

R/W	Read/write control (I)
CS	Chip select (I)
RS	Register select (I)
E	Enable (usually ph2 clock) (I)
RES	Reset (I)
CLK	Clock
HSYNC	Horizontal synchronous pulse (O)
VSYNC	Vertical synchronous pulse (O)
CUR	Cursor enable
LPSTB	Light pen strobe
DSPTMG	Blanking signal

Internal registers

With only one register select input the 6845 can directly address two registers but there are in fact nineteen registers in the chip. To handle this situation one register is used as an address register and is selected when RS is low. One of the remaining eighteen registers is accessed when RS is high. The actual register selected is determined by the data held in the address register. The functions of the eighteen registers are:

R0 Total number of characters/line period including flyback time.
R1 Number of characters/line displayed

R2	Horizontal synchronous pulse position in line period
R3	Synchronous pulse width
R4	No of raster lines in picture
R5	Fine adjustment of number of lines
R6	Number of raster lines displayed
R7	Vertical synchronous position
R8	Interlace control
R9	Number of raster lines per displayed symbol
R10	Cursor control
R11	Cursor control
R12	Start address in display memory (MS)
R13	Start address in display memory (LS)
R14	Cursor position (MS)
R15	Cursor position (LS)
R16	Light pen position (MS)
R17	Light pen position (LS)

Registers R0–R11 are write only, registers R12–R15 are read/write and registers R16–R17 are read only.

In a simple text only display the RA0–RA5 address lines would be used to address a character generator ROM. The output from this ROM is then fed to a video shift register to produce the required sequence of dot signals for the video output. The display RAM is generally part of the RAM used by the CPU itself and some form of multiplexer is required to switch between the CPU address bus and the CRTC address bus to provide an actual address for the memory chips.

Scart connector

Many television sets are now designed to be used as monitors for home computers and for input of direct video from other sources such as video recorders. These sets are generally fitted with a SCART connector if they are designed for use in Europe. This connector allows direct input of either composite video signals or RGB analogue inputs. The connection details are;

Pin	Signal
1	Audio output (right)
2	Audio input (right)
3	Audio output (left)
4	Audio ground

5	Blue ground
6	Audio input (left)
7	Blue input
8	Source switching
9	Green ground
10	Data bus
11	Green input
12	Data bus
13	Red ground
14	Data bus ground
15	Red input
16	Video blanking
17	Composite video ground
18	Video blanking ground
19	Composite video output
20	Composite video/synchronous
21	Ground and screen

15 System development

When designing any project based around the use of a microprocessor the first step must be to define as accurately as possible what the system is required to do. Once this has been done it should be possible to decide on the hardware configuration which consists of choosing the type of CPU and the circuits that surround it. Hardware development may also include mechanical design of circuit boards and cases or other enclosures. When the processor and basic hardware arrangement have been chosen the software can be developed. Software includes the programs which will control the operation of the system and also the documentation such as listings and operating manuals. Some functions of the system can often be implemented either by additional hardware or by software routines and as development progresses choices can be made to decide which option is best for use in the system.

Hardware options

The choice of the hardware for the project can be broadly broken down into four possible approaches.

1 Use of a personal computer PC.
2 Use of a single board microcomputer.
3 Use of standard boards and backplane bus.
4 Custom designed system.

Personal computers

For a project where only a few systems are to be built and the size of the equipment is not a major consideration a convenient approach is to use one of the popular home computer systems to provide the ⋯⋯⋯⋯ Hardware development is then ⋯sign of any additional circuits ⋯e the computer to the external ⋯in advantages of using a personal ⋯he cost will often be lower than ⋯rdware options and the computer ⋯he software development. The computer will have its own built in operating system and its hardware operation has already been tested.

Personal computers can broadly be divided into two groups. At the lower end are the machines based around 8-bit processors, such as the 6502 and Z80. Nowadays these computers are often looked upon as just games machines but in fact they can provide quite respectable computing power. More modern personal computer systems are usually based on 16- or 32-bit processors, such as the 8086 and 68000 types, and provide much greater computing power and higher speed than the 8-bit machines.

Of the 8-bit types the Apple II series is probably best suited for control and instrumentation projects since it provides a set of eight expansion connectors for use with interface cards and any other additions to the basic computer configuration. In most models the processor is a 6502 but the Apple IIc uses the 65C02 and the Apple IIGS uses the 65816 which is a 16-bit processor based on the 6502. These computers have a wide range of software including assemblers, compilers and debug programs which facilitate software development. There are also many standard cards available which can be used in the expansion slots to give parallel, serial and analogue input–output facilities. Another machine based on the 6502 is the Acorn BBC computer which provides a good selection of parallel and serial interfaces and has software available which would be suitable for program development.

The Sinclair Spectrum and Amstrad CPC machines are based on the Z80 processor and despite their low cost can provide very useful computing facilities. Each machine has its main processor bus brought out to a connector so that external circuits can fairly readily be interfaced to the CPU. Both types have software available which is suitable for program development using either assemblers or compilers.

Of the 16-bit computers, the IBM compatible PC is the most widely used as a business and professional machine. The PC-XT normally uses an 8088 CPU although some versions may be fitted with an 8086 or an NEC V20 or V30. The PC-AT models use the 80286 or 80386 as the CPU and provide more processing power and higher speed whilst maintaining general software compatibility. A typical machine have 640k bytes or more of memory and Microsoft MSDOS disk based operating

Like the Apple II series these machines have expansion slots which allow additional interface or other cards to be added to the basic computer. A vast range of software is available for these computers and this includes all of the programs likely to be needed for software development.

The alternative computers to the IBM PC types are all based upon the 68000 series of 16/32-bit processors. The Atari 520ST and 1040ST provide similar processing power and speed to the PC-AT type of computer but at a very much lower price. These machines have built in serial, parallel and DMA interfaces but do not have expansion slots and provide only partial access to the CPU bus. There is also a MEGA range of ST computers where the CPU and keyboard are housed in a separate units. These computers have an expansion bus which allows dedicated interfaces to be added to the machine. Memory in these machines ranges from 512k bytes in the 520ST up to 4Mbytes in the MEGA ST4. An advantage of the ST machines is that they have a built in WIMP (window, icon, menu and pointer) operating system which uses a mouse and an icon based display to make operation of the system very simple. The Commodore Amiga 500 provides similar facilities to those on the ST except that its normal operating system uses text commands although a WIMP type interface can be loaded from disk if desired. Both the ST and Amiga have excellent colour graphics displays and a wide range of software is available, including all of the packages likely to be needed for software development.

Single board computers

A number of manufacturers produce single board microcomputers based around the more popular CPU types such as the 6809, Z80, 8086 and 68000. This type of system consists of a single circuit board containing the CPU, RAM, and ROM as well as a selection of serial and parallel input–output channels and one or more counter-timer circuits. Some types may also provide analogue input and output facilities.

The ROM and RAM areas may contain empty sockets into which appropriate ROM or RAM chips can be inserted to suit the project requirements. Some boards may include a section of ROM which is already programmed with a simple monitor type operating system.

This type of system is generally suited to projects where the computer is acting as a controller for other equipment. The hardware is already designed and tested and this type of board will generally produce a system which is more compact than if a personal computer were used. For a simple project the only additional hardware needed would be a power supply and a case. If information needs to be fed into the system or output data is to be displayed then a video display terminal will also be needed.

Backplane bus systems

In this type of system a series of standard circuit cards are plugged into a backplane bus system mounted in a small chassis or rack unit. Each card contains a section of the system such as the CPU, memory, input–output, timers, power supply or perhaps special interface circuits. The arrangement is more flexible than the single board computer approach since the cards can be selected to give just those facilities needed for the project. There will also be prototyping cards available to allow custom circuits to be built. Most of the currently available systems are based upon the STE Eurocard bus system.

The cost of this type of system is generally higher than that of a single board computer but there is the advantage that the system can easily be modified or expanded to suit new requirements. This type of system can be expanded to include a disk based operating system and the facilities for software development.

Custom design

Where mass production is envisaged or where the processor system has to be incorporated into an existing piece of equipment some form of custom designed hardware is likely to be appropriate. When this approach is considered the basic hardware configuration may be tried out using a backplane bus type of system and then custom circuit boards are designed and built for the production version. Further testing and possibly modifications may be needed before the final version is completed. In some cases application specific integrated circuits (ASICs) may be used instead of standard chips in order to reduce the size of final circuit module if space is limited.

The initial cost of producing a custom designed system is very much higher than any of the alternative hardware approaches. Once mass production of the modules starts, however, the cost of a single module is likely to be much less than that of the alternative hardware schemes.

Development systems

When a personal computer is used as the basis for a project the software required can usually be developed on the computer itself and the hardware, apart from any additional interfaces, is already tried and tested. The additional hardware interfaces can generally be checked by writing small test routines and running these with the interface connected to the computer system.

When any of the other hardware approaches is used some additional equipment will be required to allow the software for the project to be written, compiled and tested. If the program in the microcomputer is to be held in ROM then for testing purposes an EPROM would normally be used and some means of writing the data into the EPROM will be required. When the program has been written and compiled it will have to be tested with the prototype hardware. To find faults in hardware operation some form of logic analyser is essential.

Software writing and the compilation of the machine code program can be carried out on almost any computer provided that it has a text editor program to generate the source code and an assembler program to convert the source code into a machine code file. If the computer uses the same processor as the target system being developed then it may also be possible to test the software as well. Where the computer uses a different processor it is still possible to generate the required machine code by using a cross assembler program. It may also be possible to carry out some tests of the software if a software emulator program is used. This type of program reads the instructions from the machine code file for the target CPU and then tells the local CPU to perform the equivalent operation. A program being executed in this way usually runs somewhat slower than it would on the target CPU but apart from timing the general action of the program can be tested by using emulation.

Testing of the program with the actual hardware can present more problems. Since most of the signals in a microprocessor system tend to be multiplexed and their timing relative to other signals is important the use of an ordinary oscilloscope to examine waveforms is of limited use in diagnosing faults. The solution is to use a logic analyser unit which may have sixteen or more inputs each of which can be used to monitor one of the signals in the target system. Usually a burst of perhaps 256 or more samples of each signal are taken with a preset time interval between samples. The results may then be displayed on a text type display as patterns of 0 and 1 states. If a group of signals represents an address or data value these signals may be displayed together as a group. An alternative arrangement is for the analyser to calculate the data value of the group of signals and display the result as a hexadecimal number. Some more advanced analysers include personality modules which allow the signals on the data and address buses to be disassembled so that the display will show the opcode mnemonic of each instruction and its associated address and also the instruction operand.

An alternative display mode is to present each logic signal as a waveform so that the analyser effectively becomes a multitrace oscilloscope. This is particularly useful for examining the relative timing between various signals in the microprocessor hardware. In this mode the analyser may also include facilities for detecting and displaying 'glitches' which are very short signal spikes caused by faulty timing in the logic circuits being tested.

The start of acquisition of the block of samples can be synchronized to events in the microprocessor hardware. Thus the block might start when a particular address occurs on the address bus or when a particular value appears on the data bus. By using a logic analyser it is possible to examine what is happening in the hardware system and thus to pinpoint where a fault is occurring.

Although hardware and software development and testing could be achieved by using a personal computer and some test equipment such as a logic analyser it is generally more convenient to use a dedicated microprocessor development system (MDS) for this purpose. An MDS consists of a dedicated computer, usually based on the same processor as the type used in the development project, with a backplane bus construction. The operating system is normally disk based and will provide a text editor for source code generation as well as assembler and compiler programs to generate the required machine code. In addition there is usually a debug program which will allow the software to be tested. An in circuit emulator and logic analyser facilities may also be provided for testing the prototype hardware. The MDS system is usually arranged so that it can be configured to have the same memory and hardware address allocations as the target prototype system. This allows the software to be tested using the MDS before trying it out on the prototype hardware. Most systems include an EPROM programming facility which allows a machine code file to be automatically transferred into an EPROM chip and then verified.

Debug programs

A debug program, sometimes called a monitor, allows the software being developed to be run under controlled conditions so that any faults in operation can be found and rectified. One useful feature is the ability to insert a 'breakpoint' into the program so that when execution reaches the breakpoint instruction the program stops executing and control is handed back to the debug program. At this point it is usually possible to examine the states of the CPU registers and contents of memory locations.

If the program is being tested using the MDS the breakpoint may be generated by inserting a software interrupt instruction in place of the original opcode at the point where execution is to be stopped. The debug program saves the original opcode and this can be re-inserted in the program so that execution can be resumed from the point at which it was stopped. When the interrupt occurs the system will usually display the contents of all of the CPU registers and the debug program will allow registers or memory locations to be examined or altered before execution of the program is restarted.

Another useful mode of operation with debug programs is single step execution in which the program is executed one instruction at a time and the contents of the CPU registers and memory can be examined or altered before the next instruction is executed. Some debug programs can also display a disassembled listing of the machine code showing the opcode mnemonics, addresses and other operands.

An alternative technique for breaking into the operation of a program is the hardware 'stop on address' system. Here the address bus signal is continuously compared with a preset address value and when a match is detected an interrupt is initiated and once again the CPU registers and memory may be examined before the program execution is resumed. Unlike the breakpoint scheme this technique does not involve alterations to the program code being executed and can be used with programs stored in ROM on the prototype hardware if an in circuit emulator is used.

In circuit emulators

When an in circuit emulator (ICE) is used the processor chip is removed from its socket in the prototype system and is replaced by an adapter probe which plugs into the socket and feeds the signals from it via a multicore cable back to the MDS. The adapter usually contains a series of buffers to reduce the effects of adding the cable. Now a processor in the MDS unit carries out the functions of the original CPU in the prototype board. In the development system the signals from the adapter lead are fed to an emulator card which normally contains the same type of CPU as that in the target system. This processor card is arranged so that it can access either the bus on the prototype card or the main system bus of the development system. The control software for the emulator CPU may be in ROM on the emulator card or it may be located in the main memory of the development system. Although it is usual for the emulator CPU to be of the same type as the CPU in the target prototype system this is not essential. Some systems use a single fast processor to emulate a number of different types of target processor by simply using an appropriate software package.

Because execution is controlled by the MDS it is now possible to use all of the features of the debug routines and the main system can also perform as a logic analyser by sampling the states of the signals on the prototype board bus system. Thus using an ICE system allows full use to be made of the MDS facilities whilst debugging the operation of the software with the actual prototype circuit board.

Programming languages

The actual instructions used by the CPU itself consist simply of numbers and writing programs directly in this form would be a very tedious and time-consuming process for any program other than a small routine containing only a few instructions. The usual procedure therefore is to write the program in a language which is relatively easy for the programmer to understand. This version of the program is called the 'source' code and is basically a text file which is generated by using either a text editor or a word processing program. Each line of the text file is usually referred to as a statement. The source file is then processed by a translation program which produces as its output an 'object' file which is basically the machine code instructions that the CPU will eventually execute.

There are two basic types of translation program which may be used to generate the executable instructions. One is a compiler which generates an output file of machine code instructions which may be used later as an executable program. The second type is an interpreter which translates the source code whilst the program is being executed by the CPU. Because each instruction has to be translated before it is executed a program using an interpreter executes at a much slower rate than a compiled program.

The simplest form of translation program is an assembler which converts each line of source code into one machine code instruction. This is known as a low-level language. Most other interpreter and compiler programs are known as high level languages in which the source code uses mathematical equations and English command words and each line of program may generate hundreds of machine code instructions.

Assembly language

In assembly language each opcode in the processor's instruction set is given a mnemonic name. Examples are LDA (load accumulator), LSR (logic shift right), ADD (add) and JMP (jump). Data variables, constants and memory addresses can be given simple names and the individual statements in the program can be identified by giving them a label. Each statement usually generates one instruction in the finished program.

The source code for an assembler normally follows a set format for each statement. The usual layout consists of four fields as follows:

Label   Opcode   Operand   Comment

The label at the start of the statement line is used to identify that statement. Labels are normally optional and if no label is required a space is usually inserted instead.

The second field contains the opcode mnemonic or an assembler directive. This is usually a three or four character code.

The third field contains the operand which may be an expression representing an address, a constant or an offset depending upon the type of instruction. The operand may in fact, contain several items in the form of an expression. Some examples of operands are:

ADDR + 2	an address
#5	a constant
(ADDR,X) + 2	an indirect indexed address
D2,D4	source and destination registers

Finally, a comment field may be added at the end of the statement line.

The individual fields of the statement are usually separated by spaces but in some early assemblers each had to start at a specific position in the line. One type of statement that does not include a mnemonic is the comment. This usually has a special symbol such as an * as its label and the rest of the line may then be used as a comment. When the source code is processed by the assembler program the comment fields and comment statements are ignored and do not produce any machine code data in the object program.

Assembler directives are extra mnemonic codes which tell the assembler program itself to perform some action and like comments these do not produce machine code data. The actual set of assembler directives will vary from one assembler to another but there are a number of common types which are found in all assemblers. Examples from a typical 68000 assembler are:

ORG	Define start address in memory
DC.B	Define a byte long constant
DC.W	Define a word long constant
DS.W	Reserve one word of memory
DS.L	Reserve a double word in memory
EQU	Define the value of a label

Variables and constants used in the program can be given simple names of perhaps six or eight characters each and this can make the operation of the program easier to follow. These names have to be defined in the program by using assembler directives such as DC.W, DS.W or, perhaps, EQU so that the assembler can allocate values or memory addresses to them as it translates the source code.

In a simple assembler the addresses allocated in memory are absolute so that the output file will always cause the program to load into exactly the same place in memory. In many programs, however, there are routines which are commonly used and it would be useful to be able to insert these into a new program. If these program modules have been assembled or written with absolute addresses then they must retain the same addresses when added to the new program. This can often be inconvenient and may introduce clashes in the use of parts of the memory.

An alternative type of assembler is known as a relocating assembler. When this type of assembler is used it allocates addresses with values relative to the start of its output file. Some variables and constants may be defined within the current module but others may be externally defined and will not be given values until the whole program is linked together. In order to produce the final program file a LINKER program is used. This takes the object file for each of the modules and allocates it an address space and it also allocates addresses to all of the data locations defined within that module. For variables not defined within a module it will check the other modules until it finds a definition for that variable and then allocates the appropriate value. When all of the sections of the program have been linked a new executable object file is produced and this may be loaded into the memory and executed.

Another feature of some assemblers is the use of 'macro' instructions. Here a sequence of several statements which is used frequently in the main program may be defined as a single macro instruction and can be allocated its own pseudo opcode. The definition of the macro is usually included at the start of the source code. Now when the set of instructions is required the newly defined opcode is inserted as a statement and when the program is assembled the assembler will automatically replace the opcode with the sequence of instructions defined earlier. Variables used in the sequence of instructions within the macro may be defined in the operand used with the macro-instruction opcode. The use of macros can save time in writing the source code although the final object code is unaffected.

Suppose we want to print the squares of the numbers from 1 to 10. The section of assembler source code might be written as follows for a 68000 type CPU.

```
      ORG $8000
      MOVE.W #1,D2    Set starting value in D2
LOOP  MOVE.W D2,D0    Copy D2 to D0
      JSR PRINT       Print contents of D0
      MULU D2,D0      Multiply D0 by D2
      JSR PRINT       Print contents of D0
      JSR PCRLF       Go to new print line
      CMPI.W #10,D2   Have all 10 been done?
      BEQ NEXT        Yes go to next section
      ADDI.W #1,D2    No add 1 to D2
      BRA LOOP        Go to LOOP
NEXT .....
```

Somewhere else in the program the subroutine labelled PRINT will need to be written to cause the contents of register D0 to be printed out. It is assumed here that the PRINT routine does not destroy the contents of D0. Another subroutine PCRLF must also be written to print a carriage return and line feed after each set of results has been printed out.

BASIC language

The most popular language on the 8-bit personal computers is BASIC (beginner's all purpose symbolic instruction code) which was originally developed in the USA as a teaching language for students.

In its usual form BASIC is an interpreter type language in which the source code is actually translated into machine code routines as the program is executed. Recently a number of compiled versions of BASIC have been produced which generate executable machine code object files. The advantage of using a compiled BASIC is that the compiled programs will run some ten to fifteen times faster than the equivalent program using a BASIC interpreter.

An important advantage of the interpreter mode of BASIC is that it is easy to edit source code and quickly try the program without having to spend time in compiling and loading to produce an executable machine code form. The main disadvantage of BASIC is that because it is interpreting the source code as it executes, the speed of operation of BASIC programs is generally much slower than that for a compiled machine code program.

BASIC is executed one statement line at a time. In most versions of BASIC each statement line is numbered and lines are executed in numerical sequence. The exception to this rule is when a subroutine is called or the program is told to jump directly to a specified line. Usually line numbers are increased by ten on successive lines when the program is initially written. This allows the possibility that in the event of extra statements being required in a section of the program the extra lines can be slotted in by simply giving them intermediate numbers between those of the preceding and following lines.

One problem with BASIC is that a number of different dialects of the language have been produced since each computer manufacturer has tended to develop its own version of the original BASIC language. As a result programs written for one version of BASIC will usually need to be altered to make them run with a different version of BASIC. Some of the latest versions of BASIC do not use line numbers and allow statements to be labelled with alphanumeric labels.

An example of a BASIC program is:

```
10   REM calculate squares of numbers 1 to 10
20   FOR N = 1 TO 10
30   A = N * N
40   PRINT N,A
50   NEXT N
60   END
```

FORTH language

An interesting language that was originally devised for controlling telescopes at an observatory is called FORTH. This language is particularly designed for use in control applications.

In FORTH data manipulation is orientated around the use of a data stack. A second stack is used to handle program control for subroutines and jumps. The actual program statements may look unfamiliar to those programmers used to using BASIC. Unlike BASIC which uses conventional mathematical equations the FORTH statements are written using the reverse polish format in which the data values are followed by the function to be performed. This type of format is often used in digital calculators. Thus to add the numbers 3 and 4 together the statement would be:

3 4 +

In operation the number 3 is pushed to the top of the stack. Then the number 4 is pushed on to the stack. When the + sign is detected the top two numbers are pulled off the stack and added together and the result is pushed back to the top of the stack. Note that in the statement each item is separated from the next by a space.

The top number on the stack can be duplicated by using the command DUP which results in the same number appearing in the top two positions on the stack. If we want to calculate the square of a number the instruction becomes:

N DUP *

which effectively multiplies the number N by itself.

New instructions can be defined by enclosing the code for the new instruction between : and ; so we could generate a new instruction called SQUARE by writing

: SQUARE
    DUP *
;

Now writing the word SQUARE will cause the data word at the top of the stack to be squared and the result is placed at the top of the stack. When a new FORTH word is defined in this way it is compiled as a set of linked machine code modules and stored in the FORTH library which is called a vocabulary. Now when the new word is executed the program simply jumps to the machine code routine for that word in the vocabulary. The entire program can be defined as a FORTH word and compiled in this way so that when the program is executed it will simply perform a chain of machine code routines and will not be much slower than a machine code program generated using assembler.

The program to produce squares of numbers from 1 to 10 now using FORTH might be written as:

```
: SQUARES
10 1 DO
I DUP * .
LOOP
;
SQUARES
```

Now the whole program is defined as a single FORTH word called SQUARES and executing this word will cause the calculation and printing of the squares of the numbers from 1 to 10. The FORTH word . causes the word at the top of the stack to be output.

C language

Another language which has become very popular in recent years is known as the C language. This language was originally devised as a medium-level language for writing operating systems. It allows the inclusion of machine code modules but also provides many of the features of high-level languages such as BASIC and Pascal. The C source code is usually compiled into assembly code and then assembled to generate the final executable program. Programs can be written as modules and the more commonly used functions are compiled and stored in libraries. These library functions can be included when the program is compiled.

The C compiler itself is often a compromise solution and does not always produce the most efficient machine code. To overcome this any sections which are time critical could be written as assembly code modules and incorporated into the final program when the various sections of compiled C program are assembled and linked together to produce the executable machine code file.

One problem with C is that it does not include checks on the logical sense of the program operation and thus will allow errors which could be totally catastrophic. Whilst this allows considerable flexibility in what can be done in a C program some care is needed in order to avoid undetected 'bugs' in the final program.

The program to calculate and print squares of numbers using C becomes:

```
#include "stdio.h"
main( )
{int n,a:
    for (n = 1; n < = 10; n = n + 1)
    {a = n * n:
    printf (n,a);}
    }
```

The include statement is used to call up the printf routine from the library and this section of code is then inserted as required when the program is compiled.

Board level bus systems

A number of bus systems have been produced for board based microcomputer systems which are assembled by plugging ready assembled circuit boards into a backplane bus in some form of rack or chassis assembly. Typical systems might consist of a CPU board, parallel I/O board, memory board and serial I/O board. Other cards could then be added to expand the system as desired. Some of the popular bus standards are STD, STE, and MULTIBUS.

The STD bus

This bus uses a 56-way double-sided edge connector with 0.1 inch spacing between contacts. The odd numbered pins run down one side of the PCB whilst even numbered pins are on the opposite side of the board.

Pin	Signal
1	+5 V power supply
2	+5 V power supply
3	Ground 0 V

4	Ground 0 V
5	− 5 V power supply
6	− 5 V power supply
7	Data D3
8	Data D7 (MSB)
9	Data D2
10	Data D6
11	Data D1
12	Data D5
13	Data D0 (LSB)
14	Data D4
15	Address A7
16	Address A15
17	Address A6
18	Address A14
19	Address A5
20	Address A13
21	Address A4
22	Address A12
23	Address A3
24	Address A11
25	Address A2
26	Address A10
27	Address A1
28	Address A9
29	Address A0
30	Address A8
31	Write control /WR
32	Read control /RD
33	I/O request /IORQ
34	Memory request /MEMRQ
35	I/O Expansion /IOEXP
36	Memory expansion /MEMEX
37	Memory refresh /REFRESH
38	Machine synch /MCSYNC
39	/STATUS1
40	/STATUS0
41	Bus acknowledge /BUSAK
42	Bus request /BUSRQ
43	Interrupt acknowledge /INTAK
44	Interrupt request /INTRQ
45	Wait request /WAITRQ
46	Non-masked interrupt /NMIRQ
47	System reset /SYSRESET
48	Pushbutton reset /PBRESET
49	System clock /CLOCK
50	Control line /CNTRL
51	Priority chain out /PCO

52	Priority chain in /PCI
53	Auxiliary ground
54	Auxiliary ground
55	+ 12 V power supply
56	− 12 V power supply

The signal abbreviations prefixed by a / sign are all active low so that a 0 input represents a true signal. The PCI and PCO lines are used for daisy chaining interrupt signals and if the board is not requesting an interrupt itself it should simply output the state of PCI on the PCO line. STATUS1 is generally used for the M1 signal in Z80 systems or the VMA signal in 6800 systems. SYSRESET is usually the power on reset line whilst PBRESET is used for manual reset from a pushbutton switch.

IEEE 1000 STE bus

This European board level bus is now becoming popular in industrial systems which use 8-bit CPUs. The boards are standard Eurocards (160 mm × 100 mm) and are fitted with a 64-pin DIN type 41612 connector. This has three rows of thirty-two pin positions each of which the outer rows a and c are used.

Pin		Signal
A1	0 V	Power supply
A2	+ 5 V	Power supply
A3	D0	Data bit 0
A4	D2	Data bit 2
A5	D4	Data bit 4
A6	D6	Data bit 6
A7	A0	Address bit 0
A8	A2	Address bit 2
A9	A4	Address bit 4
A10	A6	Address bit 6
A11	A8	Address bit 8
A12	A10	Address bit 10
A13	A12	Address bit 12
A14	A14	Address bit 14
A15	A16	Address bit 16
A16	A18	Address bit 18
A17	CM0	
A18	CM2	
A19	ADRSTB	Address strobe
A20	DATACK	Data acknowledge

A21	SYSERR	System error
A22	ATNRQ0	Interrupt request 0
A23	ATNRQ2	Interrupt request 2
A24	ATNRQ4	Interrupt request 4
A25	ATNRQ6	Interrupt request 6
A26	0 V	Ground
A27	BUSRQ0	Bus request 0
A28	BUSAK0	Bus acknowledge 0
A29	SYSCLK	System clock
A30	− 12 V	Power supply
A31	+ 5 V	Power supply
A32	0 V	Ground
C1	0 V	Ground
C2	+ 5 V	Power supply
C3	D1	Data bit 1
C4	D3	Data bit 3
C5	D5	Data bit 5
C6	D7	Data bit 7
C7	0 V	Ground
C8	A1	Address bit 1
C9	A3	Address bit 3
C10	A5	Address bit 5
C11	A7	Address bit 7
C12	A9	Address bit 9
C13	A11	Address bit 11
C14	A13	Address bit 13
C15	A15	Address bit 15
C16	A17	Address bit 17
C17	A19	Address bit 19
C18	CM1	
C19	0 V	Ground
C20	DATSTB	Data strobe
C21	0 V	Ground
C22	SYSRST	System reset
C23	ATNRQ1	Interrupt request 1
C24	ATNRQ3	Interrupt request 3
C25	ATNRQ5	Interrupt request 5
C26	ATNRQ7	Interrupt request 7
C27	BUSRQ1	Bus request 1
C28	BUSAK1	Bus acknowledge 1
C29	+ VSTBY	Standby supply
C30	+ 12 V	Power supply
C31	+ 5 V	Power supply
C32	0 V	Ground

Intel multibus

This bus system designed by Intel is used for their microprocessor development systems and single board computers. It is also used in some industrial type applications where the computer is built up from a series of standard cards plugged into a backplane bus. The bus uses an 86-way double-sided edge connector (P1) with 0.156 inch spacing between contacts. Most boards also carry a second bus connector (P2) which has sixty ways spaced at 0.1 inch intervals. This second connector is not part of the basic multibus but is used on some boards as an auxiliary connector to carry additional signals. The main bus connections are:

Pin	Signal	Function
1	GND	Ground 0 V
2	GND	Ground 0 V
3	+5 V	Power supply
4	+5 V	Power supply
5	+5 V	Power supply
6	+5 V	Power supply
7	+12 V	Power supply
8	+12 V	Power supply
9	−5 V	Power supply
10	−5 V	Power supply
11	GND	Ground 0 V
12	GND	Ground 0 V
13	BCLK/	Bus clock
14	INIT/	System reset
15	BPRN/	Bus priority in
16	BPRO/	Bus priority out
17	BUSY/	Bus in use
18	BREQ/	Bus request
19	MRDC/	Memory read control
20	MWTC/	Memory write control
21	IORC/	I/O read control
22	IOWC/	I/O write control
23	XACK/	Transfer acknowledge
24	INH1/	Inhibit RAM
25		Reserved
26	INH2/	Inhibit ROM
27	BHEN/	High byte enable
28	AD10/	Address bus bit 16
29	CBRQ/	Common bus request
30	AD11/	Address bus bit 17

31	CCLK/	Constant clock
32	AD12/	Address bit 18
33	INTA/	Interrupt acknowledge
34	AD13/	Address bit 19
35	INT6/	Interrupt 6 input
36	INT7/	Interrupt 7 input
37	INT4/	Interrupt 4 input
38	INT5/	Interrupt 5 input
39	INT2/	Interrupt 2 input
40	INT3/	Interrupt 3 input
41	INT0/	Interrupt 0 input
42	INT1/	Interrupt 1 input
43	ADRE/	Address bit 14
44	ADRF/	Address bit 15
45	ADRC/	Address bit 12
46	ADRD/	Address bit 13
47	ADRA/	Address bit 10
48	ADRB/	Address bit 11
49	ADR8/	Address bit 8
50	ADR9/	Address bit 9
51	ADR6/	Address bit 6
52	ADR7/	Address bit 7
53	ADR4/	Address bit 4
54	ADR5/	Address bit 5
55	ADR2/	Address bit 2
56	ADR3/	Address bit 3
57	ADR0/	Address bit 0
58	ADR1/	Address bit 1
59	DATE/	Data bit 14
60	DATF/	Data bit 15
61	DATC/	Data bit 12
62	DATD/	Data bit 13
63	DATA/	Data bit 10
64	DATB/	Data bit 11
65	DAT8/	Data bit 8
66	DAT9/	Data bit 9
67	DAT6/	Data bit 6
68	DAT7/	Data bit 7
69	DAT4/	Data bit 4
70	DAT5/	Data bit 5
71	DAT2/	Data bit 2
72	DAT3/	Data bit 3
73	DAT0/	Data bit 0
74	DAT1/	Data bit 1
75	GND	Ground 0 V
76	GND	Ground 0 V
77		Reserved
78		Reserved

79	− 12 V	Power supply
80	− 12 V	Power supply
81	+ 5 V	Power supply
82	+ 5 V	Power supply
83	+ 5 V	Power supply
84	+ 5 V	Power supply
85	GND	Ground 0 V
86	GND	Ground 0 V

Signals with a / suffix are active low.

Apple II expansion bus

This computer has an expansion bus which drives
eight sockets (slots 0–7) into which expansion cards
may be inserted. The connector is a 50-way double-
sided edge connector with 0.1 inch pin spacing.

Pin	Signal
1	I/O select (active low)
2	Address bus A0
3	Address bus A1
4	Address bus A2
5	Address bus A3
6	Address bus A4
7	Address bus A5
8	Address bus A6
9	Address bus A7
10	Address bus A8
11	Address bus A9
12	Address bus A10
13	Address bus A11
14	Address bus A12
15	Address bus A13
16	Address bus A14
17	Address bus A15
18	Read/write control R/W (Write = 0)
19	Video sync pulses (slot 7 only)
20	I/O strobe (low for addresses $C800–$CFFF)
21	Ready input to 6502
22	Direct memory access DMA (active low)
23	Interrupt daisy chain out INT OUT
24	DMA daisy chain out DMA OUT
25	+ 5 V power supply
26	Ground 0 V
27	DMA daisy chain in DMA IN
28	Interrupt daisy chain in INT IN

29	Non-maskable interrupt NMI (active low)
30	Interrupt request IRQ (active low)
31	Reset RES active low
32	Inhibit main memory INH (active low)
33	-12 V power supply
34	-5 V power supply
35	3.58 MHz clock (slot 7 only)
36	7 MHz system clock
37	System assymetric clock 2MHz
38	Phase 1 system clock
39	CPU sync from 6502
40	Phase 0 system clock
41	Device select (active low)
42	Data bus D0
43	Data bus D1
44	Data bus D2
45	Data bus D3
46	Data bus D4
47	Data bus D5
48	Data bus D6
49	Data bus D7
50	$+12$ V power supply

IBM PC expansion bus

The IBM PC and the IBM compatible clones have become established as a standard for personal computers used in industry and business applications. This computer provides an expansion bus to which external equipment could be interfaced. The bus uses a 62 way edge connector with 31 ways on each side of the board. Pin assignments for this bus are

Pin	Signal	Function	In/out
1	GND	Ground (0V)	
2	CHCK	Channel check (low = error)	Out
3	RESET	Reset	In
4	D7	Data bus bit 7	
5	$+5$ V	$+5$ V power supply	
6	D6	Data bus bit 6	
7	IRQ2	Interrupt request 2	In
8	D5	Data bus bit 5	
9	-5 V	-5 V power supply	
10	D4	Data bus bit 4	
11	DRQ2	DMA request 2	In
12	D3	Data bus bit 3	

13	− 12 V	− 12 V power supply	
14	D2	Data bus bit 2	
15		Reserved	
16	D1	Data bus bit 1	
17	+ 12 V	+ 12 V power supply	
18	D0	Data bus bit 0	
19	GND	Ground (0V)	
20	BCRDY	Ready	In
21	IMW	Memory write	Out
22	AEN	Address enable	Out
23	IMR	Memory read	Out
24	A19	Address bit 19	
25	IIOW	I/O write	Out
26	A18	Address bit 18	
27	IIOR	I/O read	Out
28	A17	Address bit 17	
29	DACK3	DMA acknowledge 3	Out
30	A16	Address bit 16	
31	DRQ3	DMA request 3	In
32	A15	Address bit 15	
33	DACK1	DMA acknowledge 1	Out
34	A14	Address bit 14	
35	DRQ1	DMA request 1	In
36	A13	Address bit 13	
37	DACK0	DMA acknowledge 0	Out
38	A12	Address bit 12	
39	XCLK4	4 MHz clock	Out
40	A11	Address bit 11	
41	IRQ7	Interrupt request 7	In
42	A10	Address bit 10	
43	IRQ6	Interrupt request 6	In
44	A9	Address bit 9	
45	IRQ5	Interrupt request 5	In
46	A8	Address bit 8	
47	IRQ4	Interrupt request 4	In
48	A7	Address bit 7	
49	IRQ3	Interrupt request 3	In
50	A6	Address bit 6	
51	DACK2	DMA acknowledge 2	Out
52	A5	Address bit 5	
53	TC	Terminal count	Out
54	A4	Address bit 4	
55	ALE	Address latch enable	Out
56	A3	Address bit 3	
57	+ 5 V	+ 5 V power supply	
58	A2	Address bit 2	
59	14MHz	14.1818 MHz clock	Out
60	A1	Address bit 1	

| 61 | GND | Ground (0V) |
| 62 | IA0 | Address bit 0 |

The TC output line pulses to 1 at the end of a DMA block transfer. IRQ4 is used by the motherboard serial interface, IRQ6 is used by the disk interface and IRQ7 is used by the parallel interface.

Abbreviations

ACC	Accumulator
ACIA	Asynchronous communications interface adapter
ACK	Acknowledge
ADC	Analogue to digital converter
ADCCP	Advanced data communication control procedure
AES	Application environment services
ALU	Arithmetic and logic unit
ANSI	American National Standards Institute
ARQ	Automatic repeat request
ASCII	American Standard Code for Information Interchange
ASM	Assembler
AUX	Auxiliary
BBS	Bulletin Board Service
BCD	Binary coded decimal
BCS	British Computer Society
BIOS	Basic input–output system
BS	British Standard
BSI	British Standards Institution
CAD	Computer-aided design
CCITT	International Telegraph and Telephone Consultative Committee
CCR	Condition code register
CERDIP	Ceramic dual in-line package
CGA	Colour graphics adapter
CLK	Clock
CMOS	Complementary metal oxide semiconductor
CODEC	Coder decoder
CP/M	Control program for microcomputers
c.p.s.	Characters per second
CPU	Central processing unit
CR	Carriage return
CRC	Cyclic redundancy check
CRT	Cathode-ray tube
CRTC	CRT controller
D/A	Digital to analogue
DAC	Digital to analogue converter
DART	Dual asynchronous receiver transmitter
DCE	Data communication equipment
DIL	Dual in-line

DIN	German Standards Institute
DIP	Dual in-line package
DMA	Direct memory access
DOS	Disk operating system
DRAM	Dynamic random access memory
DTE	Data terminal equipment
DTL	Diode transistor logic
DVM	Digital volt meter
EAROM	Electrically alterable read-only memory
EBCDIC	Extended binary coded decimal interchange code
ECL	Emitter coupled logic
ECMA	European Computer Manufacturers Association
EEROM	Electrically erasable read-only memory
EGA	Enhanced graphics adapter
EIA	Electronic Industries Association (USA)
EISA	Extended industry standard architecture
EMC	Electromagnetic compatability
EMI	Electromagnetic interference
EOT	End of transmission
EPROM	Erasable programmable read-only memory
EROM	Erasable read-only memory
FAT	File allocation table
FCS	Frame check sequence
FDC	Floppy disk controller
FET	Field effect transistor
FIFO	First in first out
FM	Frequency modulation
FPLA	Field programmable logic array
FP	Floating point
FPU	Floating point unit
GDP	Graphic display processor
GEM	Graphics environment manager
GPIB	General-purpose interface bus
Hex	Hexadecimal
Hz	Hertz
HDLC	High-level data link control
HMOS	High-density metal oxide semiconductor
HPIB	Hewlett Packard interface bus
I/O	Input/output
IBM	International business machines
ICE	In circuit emulator
IEE	Institution of Electrical Engineers

	(UK)
IEEE	Institution of Electrical and Electronic Engineers
ISO	International Standards Organisation
k	kilo ($\times 1000$)
K	kilo, binary ($\times 1024$)
LCD	Liquid crystal display
LED	Light-emitting diode
LF	Line feed
LIFO	Last in first out
LSB	Least significant bit
LSI	Large scale integration
m	milli ($\times 10^{-3}$)
M	Mega ($\times 10^6$)
M	Mega, binary ($\times 2^{20}$)
MCA	Microchannel architecture
MCU	Microcomputer unit
MFM	Modified frequency modulation
MFP	Multifunction peripheral
MIDI	Musical instrument digital interface
MMU	Memory management unit
MODEM	Modulator/demodulator
MON	Monitor
MOS	Metal oxide semiconductor
MOSFET	MOS field effect transistor
MPU	Microprocessor unit
MSB	Most significant bit
MSD	Most significant digit
MSI	Medium scale integration
MUX	Multiplexer
n	Nano ($\times 10^{-9}$)
NLQ	Near letter quality
NMOS	N-channel metal oxide semiconductor
NOP	No operation
NRZ	Non return to zero
NRZI	Non return to zero invert
OEM	Original equipment manufacturer
OPCODE	Operation code
OSI	Open systems interconnection
p	Pico ($\times 10^{-12}$)
PAL	Programmed array logic
PC	Program counter
PC	Personal computer
PCM	Pulse code modulation
PIA	Peripheral interface adapter
PIO	Programmable input–output
PIT	Programmable interval timer
PLA	Programmable logic array

PLL	Phase locked loop
PMOS	P-channel metal oxide semiconductor
PPI	Programmable parallel interface
PROM	Programmable read-only memory
PSW	Processor status word
PTM	Programmable timer module
R/W	Read/write
RALU	Register and arithmetic logic unit
RAM	Random access memory
RISC	Reduced instruction set computer
RND	Random
ROM	Read-only memory
RTL	Resistor transistor logic
RX	Receiver
RZ	Return to zero
S/H	Sample and hold
S/N	Signal to noise
SAR	Successive approximation register
SBC	Single board computer
SCRN	Screen
SDLC	Synchronous data link control
SI	International system of units
SIO	Serial input–output
SP	Stack pointer
SRQ	Service request
SRAM	Static random access memory
SSDA	Synchronous serial data adapter
SSI	Small scale integration
TTL	Transistor transistor logic
TTY	Teletype
TV	Television
TX	Transmitter
UART	Universal asynchronous receiver transmitter
ULA	Uncommitted logic array
USRT	Universal synchronous receiver transmitter
USART	Universal synchronous asynchronous receiver transmitter
V	Volt
VDI	Virtual device interface
VDU	Video display unit
VGA	Video graphics array
VIA	Versatile interface adapter
VLSI	Very large scale integration
VMA	Valid memory address
W	Watt
WIMP	Window icon menus pointer

X	Crystal
XTAL	Crystal
Z	Impedance

Useful addresses

Computers Solutions Ltd,
Canada Road, Byfleet, Surrey KT14 7HQ
(Novix FORTH processors)

Hitachi Europe Ltd,
21 Upton Road, Watford, Herts WD1 7TB
(6800, 68000 series processors)

Inmos Ltd,
1000 Aztec West, Almondsbury, Bristol BS12 4SQ
(Transputers)

Inmos Corp.
PO Box 16000, Colorado Springs, Colorado 80935
USA
(Transputers)

Integrated Device Technology Inc.,
3236 Scott Blvd, Santa Clara, California, USA
5 Bridge Street, Leatherhead, Surrey KT22 8BL
(R2000/3000 RISC processors)

Intel Corp. (UK) Ltd,
Pipers Way, Swindon, Wilts SN3 1RJ
(8085, 8086, 8048 series processors)

Intel Corp.
3065 Bowers Ave, Santa Clara, California, 95051
USA
(8085, 8086, 8048 series processors)

LSI Logic,
1551 McCarthy Blvd, Milpitas, California, USA
Grenville Place, The Ring, Bracknell, Berks
RG12 1BP
(R2000/3000 and SPARC RISC processors)

Motorola Semiconductors,
Fairfax House, 69 Buckingham St, Aylesbury,
Bucks HP20 2NF
PO Box 20912, Phoenix, Arizona, USA
(6800, 68000 series processors)

National Semiconductor (UK) Ltd,
The Maple, Kembrey Park, Swindon, Wilts
SN2 6UT
(NSC800 and other processors)

National Semiconductor,
2900 Semiconductor Drive, Santa Clara,
California, USA

NEC Electronics (UK),
Cygnus House, Linford Wood Business Centre,
Sunrise Parkway, Milton Keynes, Bucks
MK14 6NP
401 Ellis Street, Mountain View, California, USA
(V series processors)

Novix Inc.,
19925 Stevens Creek Blvd., Suite 280, Cupertino,
California, 95015, USA
(Novix FORTH processors)

Rockwell International
4311 Jamboree Road, Newport Beach, California,
USA
(6500 series processors)

SGS Thompson Microelectronics,
Planar House, Parkway, Globe Park, Marlow,
Bucks SL7 1YL
(6800, 68000, Z80, Z8 processors)

Texas Instruments Ltd,
Manton Lane, Bedford, Beds MK41 7PA

Texas Instruments Inc.,
MOS Products Division, Houston, Texas 770011,
USA

VLSI Technology Inc.,
486-488 Midsummer Blvd., Saxon Gate West,
Milton Keynes, Bucks MK9 2EQ
1109 McKay Drive, San Jose, California 95131,
USA
8375 South River Parkway, Tempe, Arizona
85284, USA
(Acorn RISC processor)

Western Design Center Inc.,
2166 E. Brown Road, Mesa, Arizona, USA
(25816 processor)

Index